HAUNTED
LIVERPOOL

For Niki Ireland, with love

© Tom Slemen 2007

Published by The Bluecoat Press, Liverpool
Book design by March Graphic Design Studio, Liverpool
Printed by Universities Press, Belfast

ISBN 1 904438 56 3

Tom Slemen
HAUNTED
LIVERPOOL 14

The Bluecoat Press

CONTENTS

ARAMINTA

Before it closed its doors for good in the approaching shadow of the gargantuan Grosvenor Paradise Project, I was a regular visitor to that fabulous dusty labyrinth of quirky little shops which was Quiggins. Early in 2006, I happened to be browsing in one of the fascinating little flea markets in the building when I came across an absolute treasure; a small book with a mildewed cover, containing yellowed old newspaper clippings and handwritten notes from Victorian times. The book's theme was vampires in Lancashire, and the author was anonymous. It couldn't have come to a better home!

From my own previous research I had long known about an alleged vampire being at large in Liverpool in 1680; a blood-sucking farmer had decided to kill himself after his condition had compelled him to murder his wife and drink her blood. In a bizarre twist, the authorities ordered that his body be buried face down at the cross roads of Rupert Lane, Breck Road (formerly Breck Lane), Heyworth Street and Everton Road. An enormous wooden stake was driven through the corpse to 'prevent him rising', and the staked skeleton still lies in the same place today.

The chronicle of Lancashire vampires mentions a 'bloodsucking specimen of the Lost Race of Homo Sapiens' which perpetrated a number of outrages around the time of the first siege of Liverpool in 1643, during the power struggles between Charles I and Parliament. The vampiric individual was said to have bitten the necks of a number of women in the town, and was duly captured and transported in chains to Liverpool Castle (which stood where Derby Square is now). The weird-looking man somehow managed to slip from his shackles during the journey, and vanished into the night.

Flipping the pages forward we come to a Victorian vampire hunt which all started in the autumn of 1894 at Windermere Terrace, near Prince's Park in Toxteth. A widow, referred to as Mrs Penny, awoke in the dead of night, unable to move, as something bit into her neck and back. The last thing the widow remembered before she passed out, was the sickening sensation of blood being drawn from her body. Waking with a start the next morning, she vividly recalled the terrifying incident and wondered if it had been a particularly vivid nightmare, until she felt something wet and sticky on her nightgown and then saw that her sheets and pillowcase were drenched in blood. She gingerly touched her neck and shoulders and recoiled in horror when she felt wounds and clotted blood. A doctor was summoned and found four puncture marks which he was at a loss to explain. Such wounds were outside his experience and his best conjecture was that a sadistic intruder had stabbed Mrs Penny in the neck and back, but the widow insisted that she had felt his lips against her skin, as well as the awful sensation of the blood being siphoned out of her body before she blacked out.

The mystery deepened on the following evening when screams were heard coming from the nearby Convent of the Faithful Companions of Jesus. It turned out that someone had tried to attack one of the nuns after climbing in through a window and had fled through another second floor window after the nun had let out a scream. Police believed the culprit to be a maniac, and never dreamt that the bloodsucker was something that had been reported for thousands of years in every culture upon this earth – a vampire. Extra policeman were put on the beat around the Prince's Park area, but the blood-sucking assailant outwitted them and struck in another part of the city on the night of Sunday 14 October.

A full moon hung high in the sky that night, and at one o'clock in the morning, a jaundiced fog drifted in from the Mersey. At around 1.15am, Mr Edward Blair, a cricket bat manufacturer of Number 79A Duke Street, was awakened by the sounds of women screaming coming from somewhere nearby. He ran to his window and flung open the sash just in time to catch a glimpse of an amorphous black shape flying eastwards at treetop level along Upper Duke Street towards Canning Street, before it became lost to sight in the swirling fog. Minutes after witnessing this alarming spectacle, he saw PC Tom Norris come panting up Duke Street. The policeman had heard the screams from as far away as Hanover Street, where he had been walking his beat. He located the source of the screams at 177 Duke Street where, after being ushered in by a trembling maidservant, he was confronted by a group of hysterical women; the Davies sisters and their cousin Hannah Griffiths. Hannah, being the most composed of the three, told an incredible tale to the young policeman, which was later backed up by the testimony of her cousins.

At midnight, Hannah had awakened feeling unaccountably breathless, and had therefore opened her window to let in the crisp night air, but by one o'clock the thick fog was infiltrating the room, so she got up to close the window – and as she did so, in a corner of the bedroom, she was startled to see a woman with a pale ghastly face, dark staring eyes and long, pitch-black hair She was clad in a strange black robe that ran to the floor where it trailed about her in folds.

Hannah screamed, and turned to run for the door, but the sinister intruder darted across the room and seized Hannah in a vice-like embrace. She threw her on to the bed and sank her teeth into the side of her neck, and was just starting to draw blood when the Davies sisters burst into the room, alerted by Hannah's screams. The sisters gasped in horror at the sight of the thing that was pinning their cousin to the bed. One of them clubbed the eerie assailant on the head with a heavy brass candlestick, but she didn't flinch. Meanwhile, summoning every ounce of strength in her body, Hannah struggled like a wild thing to rid herself of the vile, blood-sucking woman, but the wiry looking female seemed to possess super-human strength and wouldn't budge.

Elizabeth Davies, recognising that the thing on top of her cousin was possessed in some way, rushed to fetch the Bible from the bedside table in her room, and returned holding the Holy Book out in front of her.

"In the name of Our Lord, depart!" she screamed, and for the first time the fiend looked up to reveal its horrifying face. Its features contorted horribly, and blood dripped from its twisted mouth before it flitted away from the bed – and dived out of the window.

A doctor treated Hannah's neck wound – two neat puncture marks – but was unable to explain what type of being could have inflicted the injury. He gave no credence to the far-fetched tale the girls had told him. The strange case was passed into the hands of sergeants William Foster and Irwin McGhee, who were based at Lark Lane police station. Foster believed that a mentally deranged female attacker was to blame for the assault on Hannah Griffiths, but Irwin McGhee was a devout Catholic and an avid student of the supernatural, and he was convinced that a true vampiress was at large ...

And so, Foster and McGhee were assigned to the peculiar case of the 'Night Attacks' – and no two men so unlike one another in character had ever been forced to collaborate so closely before, yet they were required to work together in an effort to unravel the bizarre mystery that had been haunting night-time Liverpool that autumn in 1894. The facts of the case so far were those described above.

"You mark my words, Foster, a vampire is behind all this," said Irwin McGhee, sitting at his desk at Lark Lane police station. "That's for sure."

He was reading an old leather-bound volume by Dom Calmet, an eighteenth century authority on vampirism.

"You know as well as I do, McGhee, that Hannah Griffiths was telling lies; no one can jump out of a second floor window without sustaining serious injury which would stop them from escaping. We couldn't find any trace of the person she described. A man friend must have inflicted those injuries and she will have been lying to cover up for him. Let's face it we see it all the time, but what a cock and bull story to concoct as a cover-up, and you've swallowed it hook, line and sinker!"

"Then what about the nuns? Were they lying as well?" McGhee asked.

On the desk he had a crucifix, a rosary and small phial of holy water which he constantly rearranged, as if seeking some kind of insight, or reassurance from the holy objects.

Foster took a swig of whiskey from his hip flask and shook his head, his face betraying the deep cynicism he felt for McGhee's religiosity.

"At the risk of insulting your Catholic mentality, my friend, nuns are only human like the rest of us, and when they heard about the blood-sucking maniac a few doors away, they had to get in on the act. It stands to reason, they must be bored out of their tree praying from morning till night, in that draughty old convent. I'd drive anyone one daft."

McGhee grew purple in the face at this slur on the nuns' characters; he had always been brought up to treat all nuns with the utmost reverence, as if they had a direct line to God.

"You insufferable fellow! How on earth could it possibly profit them? Wake up, man," he seethed, glaring at his colleague. "Something is taking place on the streets of Liverpool that is beyond your ken, and unless you start taking this case seriously, you may as well go home right now."

"All right. Keep your hair on." Then, after a thoughtful pause, Foster asked, "What do you have there? What's in that old book you've got?"

McGhee explained the nature of the vampire, its history, and even local legends of the ancient sanguinarians. McGhee had studied the supernatural since he was a youth of sixteen, and he had heard some very eerie tales of vampires in Liverpool from his Irish grandfather.

"At a cemetery in Everton there is said to be a female vampire," said McGhee solemnly. "I have noticed that the cover of her tomb has been disturbed periodically, and it is my belief that she is behind these recent attacks."

"Now you really are having me on," laughed Foster, but, nevertheless, midnight found the two policemen picking their way through the graves at the Everton cemetery in a thick fog. The long, sopping wet grass had soaked through their shoes and the bottom of their trousers and the night air was chilling them to the marrow.

"We'll catch our deaths here if we're not careful," laughed Foster, rather pleased with his little pun.

"Ha ha, very funny. Don't you ever take anything seriously, you buffoon? We're dealing with matters of life and death here and all you can do ..."

"Life and death ... brilliant! You have got a sense of humour after all," and Foster's laughter echoed round the gravestones.

Eventually they arrived at the very tomb where the suspected vampire was said to be buried. McGhee stood by with an iron spike and a hammer as the muscular Foster, suddenly serious now, bravely lifted the loose slab and slid it across the top of the tomb. A lantern was raised to reveal a badly disintegrated coffin from which a skeletal hand protruded. Having established that the coffin was still occupied, the slab was respectfully replaced and the pair left the graveyard as quickly as they could.

When the sergeants got back to Number 80 Lark Lane, the desk sergeant introduced them to a man who said he knew exactly who the vampire was and also where she lived. However, before the introduction, PC Blackburn, realising that the two sergeants had obviously just been through a bit of an ordeal, dutifully brought them two steaming mugs of cocoa and sat them before the roaring station fire. When he judged that they were sufficiently recovered, he told them a curious thing.

A drunken but well spoken gentleman had come into the police station at half-past eleven, asking to talk to someone about the peculiar goings-on at Duke Street. The man claimed to have been sent by Edward Blair, one of the witnesses to the recent strange incident. The man just about managed to give his name as Edwin Thompson, but had been so heavily intoxicated, that PC Blackburn had put him into the holding cells to sleep off his alcoholic stupor. Foster and McGhee hurried to the cells where the shabby-looking man was stretched out on a bench, snoring noisily. Shortly after he was roused, he squinted at the sergeants who could see that he was struggling to remember where he was. However, after a glass o water he was able to give his full particulars, which came as something of a shock, because he turned out to be an eccentric gentleman of considerable wealth who lived at Number 20 Canning Street. He then proceeded to tell the policemen a remarkable tale.

For the past month he had observed a 'phantasm' entering and leaving the house opposite his own after dark. That house – Number 23 – was the residence of a rich gentleman by the name of George Lawson, and night after night, Mr Thompson, his brother, and several servants had watched the eerie comings and goings of a shadowy, gaseous form that floated through the air and entered the roof of Lawson's home. Sergeant Foster was at a loss to know what to make of the weird account, but his colleague McGhee was certain that Thompson had seen the vampire responsible for the series of nocturnal attacks in the city.

On the following morning, Foster and McGhee paid a visit to George Lawson and informed him that burglars had been spotted on his roof, trying the skylight. During the house call, Lawson appeared nervous and agitated, as if he was hiding something.

That night, Foster and McGhee were to be found in a room at Edwin Thompson's house, keeping watch on Lawson's Georgian residence across the street. Shortly after midnight, both policemen suddenly stiffened when what appeared to be a wisp of dark smoke drifted up from the roof slates. The vapourous mass expanded steadily and rose up from the rooftop, leaving a faint misty trail in its wake. William Foster strained his eyes as he watched the apparition slant upwards into the night sky, heading north. It was soon lost to sight. The two sergeants looked at one another, stuck for words for a moment.

Minutes later, a quarter of a mile away, in Abercromby Square, a widowed woman in her fifties, Magdalene Gee, was startled out of her sleep when the veranda doors of her bedroom suddenly burst open. Before her eyes a dark amorphous mist rapidly condensed and solidified into the form of a woman in black. The stranger's face was deathly pale, and in contrast had staring, jet-black eyes. She hovered silently towards Magdalene, and the widow, sensing a palpable aura of evil about the terrifying phantom, grasped the crucifix hanging from the chain around her neck with a trembling hand, then thrust it out towards the supernatural intruder. The demonic female backed away baring long pointed teeth as she did so – then once again dissolved into a body of dark vapour, which drifted out of the window into the night air.

Magdalene let out a shriek and ran out of the bedroom, and her cries of alarm alerted PC Fred Mattinson, who happened to be passing by the house on his beat. At half-past twelve, Foster and McGhee witnessed the smoky form returning to Number 23 Canning Street via its roof. The news of the sinister Abercromby visitation reached Lark Lane via the Dale Street Detective Office on the following morning. It was time for Foster and McGhee to pay Mr Lawson another visit.

They arrived at the house of the Canning Street millionaire just after 4pm as the purple shade of the October dusk was reaching over the eastern skies of the city. Once again, the sergeants used the pretence of roof burglars being at large to explain their visit, but Mr Lawson was a canny man, and although he granted the policemen access to inspect his attic for signs of attempted entry, he had a good idea what the visit was really about – the vampiric attacks on the women of Liverpool. Lawson offered the sergeants a sherry, engaged them in small talk, and seemed only too glad when it was time for them to leave.

On the following morning, at 11am, Foster and McGhee called at the home of Edwin Thompson, the well-to-do but perpetually intoxicated gentleman who lived across the street from Lawson. A butler ushered them into the sitting room, and almost a quarter of an hour elapsed before Thompson appeared. He stood swaying before the fire and Foster asked him if he had seen any unusual guests visiting Lawson's home of late. Thompson leaned on the mantelpiece for support, spent a moment in agonised contemplation, then revealed that a woman in odd funereal clothes had arrived at Lawson's house one Sunday several months ago. He had never seen her before and when he came to think of it, had never seen her leave the residence. All of a sudden, Thompson pointed to the window and shouted, "By Jove! There! There she is!"

The two sergeants ran to the window. A carriage had pulled up outside Lawson's house, and the millionaire and a strangely dressed woman in black – with her face covered by a dark veil – were descending the front steps. Foster and McGhee flew out of the sitting room and were on the street in seconds. They hailed a hansom cab and instructed the driver to follow the carriage trundling down Canning Street. The pursuit stretched to the Pier Head, where, it transpired, Lawson and the woman intended to board a ship bound for Ireland.

Foster and McGhee confronted Lawson, expecting him to threaten them with harassment, but instead, he became melancholic, and told them a bizarre story. The woman with him was his lover. Her name was Araminta, and she had been driven out of Hungary because she was the last of a line of vampires. She despised being a vampire, and no man she had ever loved had been able to accept her for what she was – until she met Lawson. Now the couple wanted to settle in Ireland for a while before going on to America.

As George Lawson was giving this eerie account, Sergeant Foster gazed at the pale ghostly face of Araminta, faintly visible through her veil – and he was staggered to see jet black tears dripping from her eyes as she silently wept. Foster reached for his service revolver, but McGhee seized his hand and shouted, "No!"

"We can't let them go somewhere else where this thing will suck the blood out of other people!" said Foster, who now had no lingering doubts in his mind as to the existence of vampires.

His fear and loathing of the blood sucking creatures were driving him on to shoot the woman. He roughly pushed McGhee away and aimed the gun at the woman in black, who stood there calmly awaiting her fate. Lawson then flung himself into the firing line of the revolver, and tried to throw a punch at Foster, but missed.

Araminta seized her chance. Before anyone could stop her she had climbed over the safety chain and on to the Landing Stage. McGhee, suddenly spotting her, cried, "No!" but she jumped into the freezing October river anyway. Foster fired the revolver repeatedly into the murky waters, and when he was sure that the barrel was empty, McGhee dived in to try and save the woman – but only managed to recover her clothes. Lawson stared forlornly into the Mersey, sobbing pitifully. Araminta was never heard from again.

Had the self-tormented vampiress really committed suicide, or had she simply made an escape to then create fear and havoc elsewhere? We will probably never know.

THE GHOSTLY BABY-SNATCHER
OF CHURCH STREET

In the 1990s, a record store was getting ready to open on Church Street, and a gang of electricians and plasterers were putting the finishing touches to the premises one evening, putting in overtime to meet a deadline. The time was around 6.30pm, and a group of the workers left the premises in order to grab a bite to eat at McDonalds on the corner of nearby Lord Street. Two security men stayed behind in the Church Street premises, one upstairs, and one on the ground floor, which was in darkness, the wiring having not yet been finished. The guard downstairs, a man named Phil, glanced at his watch, wondering when the electricians and plasterers would return. The time was almost 7 o'clock. Working in the darkness presented no problem for Phil, he was used to it, and his thoughts were far removed from the world of the supernatural that night, and anyway, he did not believe in ghosts or anything of that nature.

All of a sudden, the front glass plate doors of the building began to shudder violently, as if a gale force wind was battering them – even though the weather was perfectly calm that evening. At the same time as this started, a girl approached the building, and Phil noticed that her dress and hairstyle looked dated, as if she had just stepped out of the 1950s or something. In her hand she clutched a baby swathed in a white cloth. In total silence she walked straight through the locked plate-glass doors, as Phil went rigid with shock. The girl seemed to be between eighteen and twenty-three years of age, and her face was streaked with a mixture of mascara and tears. She was still sobbing faintly. She walked straight through Phil, apparently unaware that he was even there. He recoiled in terror, and stepped backwards with such force, that he slammed his back into some metal shelving. The girl carried on walking in a straight line into the dark depths of the store before vanishing into thin air.

His heart pounding, Phil struggled to make sense of this vanishing act – then he received his second shock. Loud bangs on the locked plate-glass doors startled him and he spun round to find that it was just the electricians and plasterers, back from McDonalds. When Phil told them about what he had seen, they assured him that they had seen no girl approach the building. However, on

14

the following evening two plasterers both saw the mournful girl carrying the baby. She entered the store through the locked plate glass doors and then vanished into a wall.

They say the tragic ghosts of the woman and child are still seen on Church Street to this day, but no one knows whose ghosts they are. I have been told that in the 1950s a young woman lost her baby and became deeply depressed. One day she was in Church Street wandering aimlessly in a sorrowful haze, when she saw a baby who had been left outside a shop in its pram by its mother, (as most women used to do in those more trusting days). At the sight of the sleeping baby all the anguish of her loss welled up inside her and without thinking she snatched the baby from its pram and ran off. Her mind must still have been in turmoil because she ran straight in front of a bus and was knocked over, killing the child instantly and fatally injuring the woman, who managed to stagger into a certain well-known store before dropping dead, still holding the baby, in front of many horrified shoppers.

I have yet to trace this tragic incident in the city's archives, but as ever, I'll keep on trying and until then will keep an open mind.

GRISMELDA AND THE CHILDWALL GOBLIN

I have written about leprechauns before in my books, and in *Strange Liverpool*, I devoted an entire section to these strange creatures, entitled 'The Summer of the Leprechaun' – which documented the so-called 'Little People Mania' which broke out in the North West and other parts of the UK in July 1964. Little leprechaun-like figures were seen at a bowling green in Kensington that year, and also in the vicinity of St Chads and St Mary's in Kirkby. They were seen on Edge Lane, in Sefton Park, Newsham Park, Abercromby Park, the University Green off Oxford Street, Bluebell Woods in Fazakerley, Stanley Park, and Childwall Woods. Some put the sightings down to mass hysteria, while others argued that the little people must be visitors from another planet, as a UFO flap was concurrent with the time of the sightings.

Folklorists I have talked to maintain that the little people have always been here amongst us, but that in the 1960s there was a temporary tectonic shift in human consciousness which allowed us to glimpse them for a while. In other words, elves, leprechauns and fairies have always lived invisibly amongst us. They have always been here, they are here now, and will remain so after the human race leaves this planet for the stars, or blows itself to Kingdom Come.

Going further back in time, there are a few reports of leprechauns and 'boggarts' – a Lancashire species of goblin – being captured and even used for nefarious reasons. Around two hundred years ago, a rather odd-looking cottage stood near what is now Wood View Road, close to Childwall Woods. This dwelling had a large fireplace, oak floorboards, wood-panelled walls, a very low ceiling with criss-crossing beams, five-foot-tall doorways, slate flagstone floors and a magnificent curved oak staircase. It was inhabited by a reclusive and diminutive man known only as Eggle – probably a Norse first name. Eggle was completely self-reliant, keeping a cow for his milk and hens for his eggs. He was a good huntsman too, and the occasional hare, rabbit, or wood pigeon also ended up in his cooking pot.

For company, Eggle had only an old rheumatic Irish Wolfhound called Bran and a raven-black cat called Tara. This man was regarded not just as a hermit, but also as an occasional fence – a man who dealt in stolen property – but the thieves who serviced this trade weren't human – they were goblins!

One spring, Eggle was visited by his seven-year-old niece, Grismelda, whose mother was ill in Liverpool. Her father was a sailor and he was away at sea most of the time. The girl stayed with her uncle for a few months, and at the beginning of that time she witnessed something that haunted her for the remainder of her life. Grismelda woke up one night, and looked out of the window of her little room at the big full moon hanging over Childwall, which in those times, was a patchwork of fields, small holdings, hedges and woods. The little girl rubbed her eyes and squinted at the moonlit field about two hundred yards away, for she suddenly found herself doubting her senses. In the field were two figures dancing and jumping about, and these individuals were about two or three feet tall. Grismelda was a little perturbed, but like most seven-year-olds, she was curious about anything she hadn't seen before. She just had to know what these little people were.

So she crept down the old curved staircase, and when she reached the living room, she saw that the fire in the grate was still burning merrily – and in front of it Uncle Eggle's rocking chair was rocking back and forth all on its own – at least that's what Grismelda thought – until she heard something in that rocking chair singing in a low gruff voice. Then she saw this thing's little bare feet, thrust out towards the fireplace. The feet had four big toes that were round headed and pale green in colour. A wizened old face with a silvery beard and moustache peeped from behind the rocking chair. His large blue eyes glared angrily at Grismelda. He growled and snarled, "May the cat eat you and the Devil eat the cat!"

Grismelda screamed, then turned and ran upstairs to Uncle Eggle's bedroom – but his bed was empty. Her little heart pounded inside her chest as she heard the strange little old man coming up the stairs, grumbling to himself, uttering words she didn't understand, but he sounded very angry. Grismelda scrambled under her uncle's bed, rolled herself up into a ball and made herself as small as possible. She watched in horror as a pair of green four-toed feet entered the room and padded around the bed as the little old man began searching for her. Without warning he fell to his knees and peered at her under the bed with his large shiny eyes, and in his hand he held a small dagger!

Grismelda yelped and quickly shuffled out from under the other side of the bed and fled downstairs with the weird old stranger in close pursuit. He was close to catching the frightened child when Bran, her Uncle's large dog, bounded in through the front door. He barked furiously, and poor Grismelda thought he was barking at her, and she was too frightened to move, but the Irish Wolfhound rushed past her and chased the old goblin around the table and out of the cottage. Grismelda quickly pulled the bolt on the front door then breathed a sigh of relief and began to wipe her tears away. But turning round she suddenly spotted the peculiar little man's tiny boots and a pair of mismatched socks on the hearthstone in front of the fireplace. She was frightened and confused; who, or what, was the old man who had chased her? Where was uncle Eggle? As these things went round in her mind, there were three loud knocks on the door of the cottage. Grismelda drew a poker from the fire's andiron and went to the door.

"Who's there?" she cried.

"It's Uncle Eggle! Open up, girl!" came the familiar voice.

A wide smile spread across Grismelda's face, for she recognised the voice behind the door as that of her uncle. She slid back the front-door bolt and in came Uncle Eggle – followed by a troop of the strangest looking little men dressed in bizarre clothes and hats. Immediately, Grismelda remembered the little silhouettes of the people she had seen dancing in the moonlit field, and she felt butterflies in her stomach. She gasped and stood aside as the men – none of them above three feet in height – marched past her carrying a curious miscellany of objects, ranging from copper kettles to clocks, shovels, rakes, and even a dead duck!

Uncle Eggle suddenly realised that his niece was taken aback by the presence of the little fellows, and he bent down, scratched his chin, and said, "They're just friends, my dear, so don't be afraid." He then stood in the doorway, beckoning someone outside with his hand.

A faint voice on the path outside cried, "Is that damned dog still in there? I'm not coming back in till you've got rid of it."

"No, Bran's tethered in his kennel – come in here now!" Uncle Eggle replied, with a note of impatience in his voice.

And through the doorway came that barefoot goblin – yes, the very same one who had menaced young Grismelda. He blinked guiltily at the child, then glanced about in dread, expecting to see that great dinosaur of a dog once more. Having assured himself that the coast was clear, he rushed over to the rocking chair, where one of his younger colleagues was sitting, and pushed him clean off the chair and into the hearth. The nasty goblin put on his warmed socks and then his boots, then made himself comfortable in the rocking chair. He glanced back at Grismelda a few times with a raised left eyebrow and a frowning mouth. Grismelda kept close to her uncle, fearing for her safety.

Uncle Eggle picked up Grismelda and took her up to her bedroom. With great difficulty he explained that the little men downstairs were goblins and perfectly harmless, but he omitted to tell her that the things they had been carrying were stolen items from homes and farms throughout Childwall and the neighbouring areas. Nor did he tell her about the way he paid the goblins with cider, rum, whiskey and pancakes. Grismelda sniffled and told him about the nasty old goblin who had chased her, and Uncle Eggle was furious when he heard about this. He fetched the goblin concerned up to Grismelda's room and asked his niece if he was the one who had chased her. "Yes, that's him, Uncle," said Grismelda, peeping over the edge of the raised blanket at the goblin. The goblin denied that he had chased her at first, but with a little persuasion from Eggle he confessed that he was the culprit. Feeling a little braver, Grismelda accused him of running after her, and of brandishing a little knife too.

"Tully," said Uncle Eggle to the goblin. "Why did you chase my niece with a knife?"

"I hate little girls!" answered Tully after a long pause.

"Whatever on earth do you hate them for?" asked Grismelda's uncle.

Tully explained that long ago, when he was a boy goblin, two little girls had captured him. They had dressed him up in doll's clothes and played house with him and when they got bored they threw him down a well. He ground his teeth as he recalled the way that he had almost drowned in that well. Luckily for Tully, when a farmer lowered a bucket to draw up water, he clung to it and was hoisted back up to safety.

"Well this little girl is my niece and she's a good little girl, Tully, so apologise to her for your ungentlemanly conduct," Uncle Eggle told him.

Tully gritted his teeth and turned his face away from Grismelda.

"Yes, say you're sorry – now!" Grismelda snapped at Tully, pointing her finger at him.

The goblin growled and muttered something that sounded nothing like, "I'm sorry".

"In English, if you please," said Uncle Eggle.

"I said I'm SORRY!" shrieked Tully, shaking his little fists at Grismelda.

The bedroom door opened and a tiny young goblin appeared and said to Eggle: "Would you care for some roast duck for supper, sir?"

Tully stood there licking his lips at the prospect of a piece of crisp duck.

"Yes, but not for this one!" said Uncle Eggle, staring meaningfully at Tully. The old goblin ground his teeth loudly.

Despite getting off to a bad start with Tully, Grismelda came to like him, and he gradually warmed to her as well. She learned that Tully originally came from up north – from Longridge, by the Ribble Valley, but he had been hunted by cruel poachers who had killed his brother, and so he had fled down towards Wigan, where he had settled for a while, until, one day, a farmer ran over a child by accident with his cart, and claimed that the boggarts had killed him. The villagers believed the farmer and scoured the land one night with lit torches and swords, looking for boggarts to kill.

Once again, Tully hit the road, and eventually came to settle in Childwall, where he had discovered a colony of gnomes, brownies, spriggans, trolls, hobgoblins, pixies, elves and bogeys. It seemed as if Tully had been alive forever, because he told Grismelda thrilling tales about the days of long ago when knights roamed the land. Tully said he had been born in a grotto in southern France – probably near the Ardèche region – a long time ago, but just how long ago was hard to say, because the calendar of the goblin does not correspond to our year of twelve months. Tully said he had known a young William the Conqueror, and had come over to England with him during the Norman Invasion, upon which Uncle Eggle accused Tully of being a liar and said that he probably only went back as far as Henry VIII's time.

When it was time for Grismelda to return to her mother's home in the town, she was sad to leave her new found friends, and so were Tully and his kin. Fortunately, Grismelda's mother allowed her daughter to spend weekends at the cottage near Childwall Woods, and so the friendship between Grismelda and the goblin continued for many years, until one day, when she was fifteen, she received a beautiful gold ring from Tully, which, he claimed, would bring her a fine husband and ensure that she would have a large family.

Not long afterwards, Uncle Eggle died, and Grismelda met and married a handsome young merchant from Wolverhampton, where she later settled. Grismelda bore eleven children, and when she was a very old woman and coming to the end of her life, her sons took her to see the ruin of the old cottage where Uncle Eggle had once lived. The old lady shuffled into the ruin of the cottage with the help of a walking stick, and was delighted to find a fire burning in the old grate. Sitting rather morosely in front of the fire toasting his green toes, with a poker in his hand, was a familiar little old man. It was Tully, and when he saw the old woman, he jumped up in a flash, ready to flee – until she called out his name. Grismelda was very old and decrepit now, yet her eyes and voice had remained unchanged.

Tully gazed up at Grismelda in disbelief, and a lone tear descended from one of his tiny blue eyes. His face had hardly changed at all, but Grismelda's face was criss-crossed with the lines and wrinkles of old age. Tully climbed on to an old moss-covered table and clasped the trembling hand of the woman who had once been his most favourite little girl in all of the world.

"Grismelda," he sighed. "You came back."

"Hello Tully," she said, and smiled.

"What on earth happened to you? Do all those lines on your face hurt?" he asked with typical abruptness, surveying the wrinkles and crow's feet.

"No," laughed Grismelda and she explained what they were. She asked Tully not to be afraid of her sons outside, for they knew all about him, and regarded him as a friend of the family.

Grismelda, her sons and Tully enjoyed a picnic near the woods on a beautiful day, as spring was turning into summer, just like the day when a little girl had met a grumpy old goblin so many years before. As the birds in the woods sang their ancient melodies that day, Grismelda lay on the grass and quietly passed away with a smile on her face.

The sons were naturally upset, and dearly missed their mother, but there is an intriguing supernatural end to this tale. The youngest son, Oliver, who had not been present when his mother passed away, travelled up to Childwall from Wolverhampton to see the place where his mother had died and to pay his last respects. He visited the ruin of the cottage, where Great Uncle Eggle had once lived, and encountered a small dwarfish figure clad in green, warming his hands in front of a dying fire. Oliver was not afraid, but somewhat wary of the pixie, who asked him why he was trespassing.

"It's not for you to question your betters," said Oliver, condescendingly.

He looked down his nose at the little man in green and informed him that it was he who was trespassing in the home of his late Great Uncle Eggle.

"Then you're a relative of Grismelda's?" said the pixie, with curiosity in his green eyes. "I like Grismelda," he added, with a gleeful smile.

The son lowered his gaze and looked sullenly at the floor. He told the pixie that Grismelda had been his mother and that she had recently died.

"Yes, she was dead – but no more!" said the little impish-faced man.

Oliver was baffled, and assumed that the pixie was trying to comfort him, but the wee pocket-sized man slid down from the chair and told the son to follow him outside to the woods. Oliver followed the pixie deep into the woodland, where he met a medley of elves, goblins, trolls and the like, and the pixie asked each of them if they knew the whereabouts of Tully and Grismelda. Each person the pixie met said the goblin and the girl were at different places, and after a while Oliver gave up and left the pixie after calling him a liar. His mother was dead and that was that.

However, when Oliver mounted his horse on the outskirts of the greenwood, he looked back – and saw a little girl of about seven years of age, dressed all in green, and standing next to her was an elderly goblin. That girl called Oliver by his name in a strangely familiar voice – that of his late mother. She waved to him, then turned and vanished within the leafy enclosure of the woodland. It is said that the eternal child Grismelda still lives among the Fay – as the family of fairies and their kind are called – and that she and Tully and his friends still walk through Childwall Woods and play mischievous tricks on humans.

JACK NIMBLE

One of Liverpool's neglected folklore characters is the Galosher Man, also known as Jack Nimble, Sprightly Jack, and a few other nicknames. He may have been nothing more than a bogeyman, a figment of Victorian imagination, but, like Spring-Heeled Jack, the Galosher Man was widely reported throughout the city in the 1880s and 1890s, and I suspect that people in those days saw something genuinely inexplicable.

One January night in the 1890s, a gang of children noticed a funny black spot at the bottom of Great Homer Street. It was heading in their direction at great speed, and at first they thought it was someone riding a push-bike, but as the thing drew closer the children realised to their horror that it was a man in black hurtling towards them with his coat tails flying at breakneck speed. "It's Jack Nimble!" cried one of the older children, recalling the recent reports of a bizarre-looking man who ran everywhere at phenomenal, inhuman speeds, and he and the gang scattered down various alleyways.

The freakish-looking man was dressed in a top hat and a long black coat and he flew past several of the child witnesses, and was chased by a dog, but even the animal couldn't keep up with the sinister ultra-agile figure. Jack Nimble flew off into the night, his abnormally long legs a mere blur, and his arms moving back and forth like pistons. Within seconds he was lost to sight in the murky gaslit gloom, leaving the children with an incredible tale to tell that no one would believe – until Sprightly Jack put in another appearance on the following evening, that is.

On this occasion, strange shadows were seen on the back walls of the houses of Richmond Row at sunset, and several people in the neighbourhood talked of having seen an alarmingly tall man, well over six feet in height, in a topper that made him look almost a foot taller. He wore a long black cape, and set in his pallid face were a pair of large circular staring eyes. When a local barber challenged the peculiar stranger, asking him why he was lurking in the alleyway behind his shop, the man talked in a speeded up way, and not one word of his gibberish was understood. He then sped off at an amazing speed and vanished down an alleyway on Cazneau Street.

Jack Nimble was seen occasionally from that time onwards, always during the twilight hours, and particularly when the moon was full. There was a tale in the 1920s of a priest who performed the Last Rites on an old man who was believed to be the Jack Nimble figure, because he had abnormally long limbs and an almost skeletal figure. Moreover, his eyes were exceedingly large and bulging. The deceased man's clothes were pawned and for many years his elongated suit was displayed in the window of a pawnshop on Scotland Road as a curiosity to attract customers.

Who exactly was Jack Nimble? Perhaps he was a glimpse of a future type of man, for it is a fact that humans beings are becoming faster and taller with evolution, accelerated by better nutrition, medical care and living conditions. Roger Bannister became the first man to run the mile in under four minutes in 1954. He ran the mile in 3 minutes, 59.4 seconds. Since then, many athletes have continued to break records running the mile, and the current record is 3 minutes, 43.13 seconds. In fifty-three years, 16 seconds have been shaved off Bannister's record, but when will these records end? One day someone will run the Three Minute Mile, and when those times arrive, the antics of the Galosher Man won't seem quite as far-fetched.

SORCERY AT SCHOOL

Some tales I receive from members of the public initially seem ridiculously far-fetched until I research them. Even then, after I have ascertained that a yarn has a basis in reality, or indeed is perfectly true, it is often withheld from publication because it still seems too unbelievable, and I know that the reader will probably dismiss it as pure fiction. I can imagine the first Christians meeting in private, telling the stories about Jesus raising up the dead, replacing a severed ear, or feeding over five thousand people at Tabgha with a mere with five loaves and two fishes. I am not saying that these events did not happen; I happen to believe that they did, and that Jesus also really did defy death and escape from his tomb.

What I am drawing attention to is the doubting nature of the human mind. Space travel, perpetual motion, organ transplants, and time travel have all been mooted throughout history and rejected because so-called educated men disbelieved in their feasibility. For example, way back in the year 1636, an obscure writer named Schwenter, in a work entitled *Délassements Physico-Mathématiques,* described an electric telegraph which would allow the possibility of 'two persons being able to communicate with one another by means of a magnetic needle'. Baron Schilling later created this type of telegraph in 1832.

Most textbooks claim that the Scottish scientist Sir Alexander Fleming discovered penicillin in 1928, but thirty-one years before that, in 1897, Ernest Duchesne, a student at the École de Santé Militaire at Lyons, published a thesis which described his experiments in establishing the medicinal value of moulds and penicillum glaucum on harmful bacteria. The thesis was completely ignored by the scientific community. In the Middle Ages, doctors had also noted the apparently beneficial effects of Roquefort Cheese when administered to ailing patients. The veins of blue mould in the cheese were thought to contain something that had a curative property, but no one knew what that something was. I could fill an entire book about the lost opportunities of humankind which fell by the wayside because no one believed in them, but let's push ahead with the following incredible tale, told to me by two members of a coven a few years ago. Some of the names have been changed because I promised anonymity.

The adventure unfolded at a girls' school in Liverpool one wintry afternoon in January, 1968. Under the eye of the classroom clock, twenty female pupils, all aged thirteen or fourteen, struggled to silently read *Cider With Rosie* by Laurie Lee, while Miss Kate Finnegan, their beautiful thirty-year-old English teacher with her Titian-red hair and horn-rimmed glasses, gazed out at the low oppressive clouds looming in the darkening sky beyond the window panes. It was just approaching 2.30pm when the hailstones began to clatter on the classroom window panes, disguising the scratching sound that was emanating faintly from the chalkboard, but Michelle and Julie – two girls sitting in the front row – watched, incredulous, as a fragment of chalk scraped itself across the blackboard. The invisible hand rapidly drew a triangular shape that resembled a number four lying on its side – then the fragment of chalk clattered to the floor.

"Miss! Miss! Look!" cried Julie.

She stood up with one hand to her mouth and the other pointing a finger at the chalkboard. Miss Finnegan surveyed the strange Runic-looking symbol, then quickly wiped it out with the duster, and it might have been Julie and Michelle's imagination, but the English teacher looked as if she knew what that chalked sign meant. The pupils all left their desks and swarmed forward to look at the haunted chalkboard, but Miss Finnegan, mustering all her teacherly authority, ordered them back into their seats at once. The room was filled with gossiping schoolgirls; this was much more interesting than *Cider With Rosie* they thought! Five more weird glyphs were drawn on that chalkboard by the unseen hand during that lesson, and Julie and Michelle had the presence of mind to secretly copy them down in their exercise books and then did some research at the local library after school.

A wise old librarian carefully studied the copied-down symbols and said that she thought they had something to do with witchcraft. She then led the girls to a book on witchcraft trials.

"They're called witchmarks; the written language-signs of witches," Michelle told Julie, as she read from the old volume about the Pendle Witches of the seventeenth century. Michelle was a very bright girl and she eventually managed to translate the symbols that had appeared in the classroom, and shuddered at her own discovery.

"It says here that it's a death threat from one witch to another!" she gasped.

The girls thought about the message, and both came to the same conclusion:

Miss Finnegan must be the witch that the threat was aimed at! But who could possibly be the other witch; the one making the threat?

"Hey!" Michelle exclaimed. "Miss Sheldrake hates Miss Finnegan's guts because they both have their eye on Mr Fenn!"

Julie giggled. Mr Fenn, their history teacher, was exceedingly handsome and they could certainly sympathise.

"So," said Julie, "it looks like it wasn't a ghost after all who was behind all the spooky goings-on in the English class."

"No, I'm pretty sure a ghost wasn't to blame, Julie – a jealous witch was."

Julie smirked with a far-away look in her eyes and said, "Wait till I tell my nan when I get home!"

"No, you can't tell anyone, Julie," Michelle warned her. "This is witchcraft we're dealing with, and our lives could be at risk, so you must tell absolutely no one!"

On Tuesday morning, Julie and Michelle stood in the assembly hall and as all the other pupils were listening to the headmaster Mr O'Shaugnessy droning on as he told his usual boring morality tale, the two girls scrutinised the faces of the teachers standing patiently against the far wall. Sure enough, Miss Finnegan and Miss Sheldrake the art teacher were staring into one another's eyes with looks of pure hatred.

At 10am, during English class, a February fog rolled in from the Mersey and enveloped the school in a grey void of limbo. Michelle and Julie, sitting at their neighbouring desks at the front of the class, alternated glances between the text of *Little Women* and Miss Finnegan, who was what they were really interested in. She was gazing trance-like through the window into the fog-ghosted landscape. She suddenly turned to face the girls and caught them staring at her and angrily told them to keep their eyes on their books.

During the mid-morning break, when all the other pupils were in the playground, Julie and Michelle sneaked into the art room, the domain of Miss Sheldrake, the other woman they suspected of being a witch.

"What if she catches us, Michelle? She'll kill us!"

"Oh, don't worry, we saw her going into the staffroom, didn't we. She'll be there until the bell goes."

"Well, I don't like it one bit."

The two girls went over to Miss Sheldrake's desk and started looking through her things.

"Hey, look at these," said Michelle, pulling something out of one of the drawers. She showed Julie two clay figures bound together with string. "Poppets," she murmured, her researches had told her that this was the name given to the dolls witches made to represent people they wished to hex.

One of the clay figures was obviously female, and Michelle believed that it represented Miss Sheldrake. It was bound by the twine to the male effigy, which she was sure represented Mr Fenn. The twine symbolised the bond of love which the spell would exert. In the same drawer, Michelle found a box lined with indigo satin, which contained a shamrock-green-tinted crystal ball. "A spy stone," she announced.

Michelle had read up on all the tools of the witch's trade, and she smiled then uttered the ancient Aramaic command to activate the stone: "Ephphatha". Almost immediately, the two girls saw the spectral image of a familiar classroom appear in the spy stone.

"Wow," was all the spellbound Julie could manage to utter.

"That looks like the history room to me," noted Michelle.

Suddenly they heard someone cough behind them. It was Miss Laura Sheldrake. She stood in the doorway, fixing the girls with her wide sinister eyes.

"May I ask why you are rifling through my desk?" she asked, in a voice as cold as ice.

Julie and Michelle heard the bitter tone in her voice and were stuck for words. They were ordered to leave the room at once. Miss Sheldrake looked at the spy stone in its box and immediately noticed that it had been activated. Only then did she suspect that the girls possessed some occult knowledge.

Julie and Michelle were undeterred by this setback; they had set out on a mission and now they had proof that Miss Sheldrake was up to no good. They hurried down the corridor to the staffroom where they asked to see Miss Finnegan and told her what they had found in the art teacher's desk in hushed tones. Miss Finnegan was visibly shocked and amazed that the girls had been perceptive enough to realise what was going on, and she took them to the medical room – out of earshot of the other teachers – and warned them not to get involved in dangerous things that they couldn't understand.

"But, Miss, she's out to kill you," said Julie. "We just want to help."

Miss Finnegan sternly told Julie and Michelle that they'd be of more help to her if they didn't get involved. The teacher then saw a strange black cat sitting under a table in the shadows, and she pushed the girls out of the room. During the history lesson that morning with Mr Fenn, Julie and Michelle noticed the painting of the Mona Lisa behind him, and wondered if the spy stone could keep an eye on him via the eyes of the portrait; their researches had revealed that it was an old witches' trick; sometimes witches are able to see through the eyes of people in paintings and photographs.

Mr Fenn was talking about the wives of Henry VIII when he suddenly said, "Here's a little known fact. Anne Boleyn was a witch, did you know that? She used witchcraft to make Henry fall in love with her." Then all of a sudden, Mark Fenn went over to the window and watched Miss Sheldrake as she got into her car and drove off.

That same day, after school, Julie and Michelle were walking home, when something terrifying came hurtling at great speed towards them. They were passing a park in the sodden fog when they both heard a vehicle careering apparently out of control in their direction. Despite the thick fog, the Commer van had no dipped headlights like the other vehicles on the road and could only be seen as an ominous silhouette. It suddenly mounted the kerb and then accelerated towards the terror-stricken fourteen-year-olds. By a stroke of luck, quick-thinking Michelle was able to slip into the park through a gap in the railings and managed to pull her friend in after her in the nick of time. The Commer van smashed into the railings and grated its sparking sides along the wrought ironwork until it impacted into a telephone box, shattering its small panes of glass. A passing coal lorry halted, and two coalmen alighted from the vehicle and rushed over to the crashed Commer van to rescue the driver – only to find that there was no one inside the van.

The schoolgirls watched from the security of the park, both deeply shocked, and both realising at the same time that the sorceress Laura Sheldrake had tried to kill them with her evil spells. When they had recovered their equilibrium, Michelle and Julie set off for the library to formulate a plan of action. They searched through the few books in the library on witchcraft in the hope of finding some way of protecting themselves from Miss Sheldrake's malevolent influence, and Michelle eventually focused her attention on a chapter about do-it-yourself talismans like the Seal of Solomon. She gritted her teeth, stood up, and declared, "We shall become witches ourselves! We'll ask Miss Finnegan to teach us, and then there'll be three against one."

"She'll never teach us, Michelle. She told us to keep our noses out of all this, remember?" Julie said, in a resigned manner.

Michelle then went to put the books back, and returned rather quickly. She sat facing her friend across the table and whispered, "I've just thought of something. What if Miss Sheldrake isn't the bad witch after all, have you thought of that?"

"But what about the poppet we found in her desk?" Julie asked, "And that van that nearly killed us? And the death threat that appeared on the blackboard in Miss Finnegan's class?"

"Yes, but say it was all the work of Miss Finnegan, trying to make it look as if Miss Sheldrake was the evil one. Let's go to the chippy we can't think on an empty stomach. Come on!"

Julie trailed after her, like she always did, but this time she was full of deep missgivings and wondered what they were getting themselves into. But Michelle had got the bit between her teeth and nothing was going to stop her now.

"Come on, let's take a short cut across a railway track," she said.

"But we can't, Michelle. My mum said we could be electrocuted; it's dangerous."

"Oh, don't be such a bore," snapped Michelle.

At that moment Julie noticed something odd and stopped dead in her tracks; Michelle had no reflection in the glass of the library door, even though her own reflection could be clearly seen. She suddenly felt the cold hand of fear grip her stomach. Michelle turned to her and said, "Come on!" but Julie noticed that her friend's face looked different somehow. The small dark birthmark was missing from her cheek. Michelle called it her 'sleepy flea'. Julie felt sick in the pit of her stomach; this wasn't Michelle, it was an impostor – it could even possibly be Miss Sheldrake.

The schoolgirl ran back into the library and amongst the labyrinth of bookshelves she found the real Michelle – complete with birthmark – standing like a statue in a trance in a corner. Julie shook her and Michelle eventually snapped out of the spell. Julie then told her what had happened and they both ran to the front door, but the imperfect double had already left the library.

That evening, Julie broke down and cried in front of her mother. She told her all about the evil Miss Sheldrake, and her mum naturally assumed that the whole thing was just a figment of an overactive imagination, that is until she saw something appear in the mirror over the fireplace – a sinister green face – and the sight of it caused her to let out a scream.

The head was totally bald, with pointed ears and a long hooked nose, and the eyes gleamed with a sulphurous yellow radiance. The menacing entity suddenly became animated and reached out from the looking glass, extending an abnormally long thin arm towards the terrified pair. Its hand seized Julie by her long pigtail and began to drag her up towards the mirror. The girl fainted with fear, and her body became as limp as a rag doll. Her mother, although terror-stricken, grabbed Julie's arm and somehow managed to wrench the girl from the clutches of a supernatural being that is known as a 'familiar' – the shape-shifting assistant of an evil witch. After quickly depositing Julie on the sofa, her mother then grabbed the poker from the fireplace and swung it at the lime-green fiend, shattering the mirror in the process.

The smashing of the looking-glass seemed to do the trick; at last the entity was gone. Her mind racing, Julie's mother began to question what the thing in the mirror could possibly have been. In the kitchen she rifled through an old first-aid tin and located a bottle of smelling salts which she quickly uncapped and placed under Julie's nostrils. Immediately the girl started to regain consciousness and then began to cry as she remembered the demon in the mirror. Mother and daughter soon left the house, bound for Julie's grandmother's flat – a woman who had a vast knowledge of the supernatural.

Meanwhile, over at Michelle's home that night, even more terrifying phenomena were breaking out. The witching hours fall between one and three o'clock in the morning, when the occult power of the witch is at its height, and with the moon being full upon this night, this power was super concentrated. The thing stepped right out of that mirror and circled the bed, but the girl bravely lay on with the protective ancient Seal of Solomon sketched on both palms, and a set of rosary beads strung around her neck. She felt the blankets lift off her and twist themselves into the effigy of a figure with arms made of wound sheets. Michelle thrust the crucifix on the end of the rosary towards the sinister cloth apparition and it immediately slumped back on to the bed, waving its arms about.

Next, a huge grotesque brown spider appeared in a corner of the ceiling, and then crawled across towards the light fitting. Michelle began to perspire with fear, as she suffered from arachnophobia and this was the biggest spider she had ever seen. When the eight-legged horror reached the light bulb it absailed slowly towards Michelle, suspended by a fine thread. She felt intense fear in the pit of her stomach as the spider's cold hairy body landed on her bare feet. She squeezed her eyes shut and summoned all her willpower to force herself not to believe in that arachnid, because she was convinced that it was a mere illusion – a projection of Laura Sheldrake's warped mind. And as the spider inched its way over the girl's knees, it melted away.

Michelle then tried to lift herself up off the bed, but found herself unable to move. It was as if a gigantic invisible hand was pushing down on her, pinning her to the mattress. As she struggled to be free of the crushing, unseen fingers, the handle of the bedroom door twisted slowly round, and the door creaked open. A second later, the bedside lamp suddenly went out, but by the moonlight flooding into the room, Michelle was relieved to see that it was her father, but as she became accustomed to the darkness, she saw that his eyes were closed. He was sleepwalking, and in his hand he held a long carving knife. Michelle's mother followed close behind, and she also seemed to be walking in her sleep – and she was brandishing a rolling pin! The two somnambulists raised their weapons as they approached the screaming schoolgirl, who could only watch in horror as she was still being steadily pressed down into her bed by the gigantic invisible hand. Such was the crushing force, that the castor wheels on the bed eventually snapped under the strain, and Michelle gasped breathlessly as she struggled furiously to get off the mattress.

"Dad! No! Mum! Wake up!" she shouted, but the menacing zombie-like parents closed in for the kill.

Suddenly the room was illuminated by an intense indigo light, and Michelle's mother and father froze like statues. To the right of the bed, a phosphorescent woman appeared, glowing eerily in the corner. She wore a pointed hood and long translucent robes, and she began to speak in a language that the schoolgirl couldn't understand. It sounded something like Welsh, but she couldn't be sure.

"Tangnefedd," said a familiar female voice, and immediately the pressure of the gigantic unseen crushing hand was no more. The mirror demon howled loudly before slowly fading away, and Michelle's parents dropped their weapons and opened their eyes. Michelle started to recognise the face of the glowing apparition; it looked like Julie's grandmother, which didn't seem to make sense. The schoolgirl tried to speak to her but the figure vanished instantly. Michelle's mother and father believed they'd simply been sleepwalking, and Michelle was frustrated and indignant that they wouldn't believe her version of events. Incredible though it may seem, Michelle's parents seemed oblivious to the fact that she was gripped by the most awful terror. It was a mystery to all their friends that they had produced such an intelligent and resourceful daughter, because both adults were totally lacking in imagination, and they merely laughed at the idea of scaring their daughter because of the sleepwalking incident. Michelle's father, who blamed the sleepwalking episode on eating toasted cheese just before bedtime, simply trundled off back to his bedroom shaking his head.

"Come on, mother," he said. "Our Michelle would have us up all night if she could, just for the attention. Get back to sleep, Michelle, you've got school in the morning, and your mum and me have got to go to work."

Realising that it was useless to argue, or expect any help from her parents, Michelle jammed a chair up against her bedroom door and hardly got any sleep for the remainder of that night.

On the following morning, she and Julie swapped their incredible stories of the night before in the school playground.

"Jackanory, Jackanory, tell a story," mocked Mr Fenn, the history teacher, overhearing the pupils as he stood nearby smoking his pipe.

The electric bell sounded and all the girls who were scattered about the playground slowly formed into lines. With dread, Michelle and Julie set off for their next class – art, with Miss Laura Sheldrake – the teacher they now knew to be an evil witch of the Left Hand Path. This was 1968, and corporal punishment was still the norm, so when Michelle was caught whispering to Julie during the lesson, Miss Sheldrake called the two girls out to the front of the class for a caning.

"Julie, come here and hold your palm out," she hissed. "You're a rude, deceitful girl, and I'll teach you to go poking your nose into other people's business."

But Michelle intervened and cried, "No, Miss. Cane me first!"

The class chuckled; Michelle could always be relied upon to stand her own corner, even when faced with as formidable a teacher as Miss Sheldrake. Miss Sheldrake was livid at the audacity of the girl and raised the cane, ready to grant Michelle her wish with a vengeance – when she suddenly spotted the protective Seal of Solomon drawn on the girl's palm. Her reaction was immediate and dramatic, she dropped the cane and recoiled in horror at the sight of symbol, and stumbled back against her desk.

"There's only one way to disarm an evil witch!" Michelle announced, and she turned to her stunned classmates and told them, "She has to be publicly accused of consorting with Beelzebub, the Prince of Darkness! And I now publicly accuse you, Laura Sheldrake, of being an evil, wicked witch! I accuse you!"

Miss Sheldrake's face elongated alarmingly as she shrieked out of control, and her raven hair ghosted into grey. Julie trembled and cowered behind Michelle, fearing for her life, and the other pupils started to stampede out of the classroom. Michelle tried in vain to stop them, because Miss Sheldrake would only be stripped of her powers if the whole class witnessed the accusation. But within seconds, all eighteen pupils had poured out into the corridors screaming hysterically. Consequently Laura Sheldrake was given time to recover. "Now you two die!" she promised Michelle and Julie. Laura Sheldrake threw up her arms and recited what Michelle took to be a hex, then pointed her finger at the floor of the classroom. "Gehenna!" the witch shouted, and an enormous circle opened up in the floor-tiles, revealing an intense hot orange glare.

Michelle and Julie backed away, mesmerised and horrified by the slowly expanding hole with its bubbling flaming rim, like the crater of an active volcano. It looked like nothing less than the opening to the gates of Hell, and the two traumatised girls gazed down at the fiery furnaces, incandescent caverns and ashpits of this nightmarish underworld, occupied by barely visible writhing figures fathoms beneath them. Screams of torment and the agonised howls of the damned echoed through the empty classroom, and as the hole widened, desks toppled into the aperture, burst into flames, and in seconds were totally consumed by the furnace. Julie ran to the door and tried to twist the handle but it wouldn't budge. She let out a yelp as she felt something invisible grip the back of her blazer and pull her towards the yawning mouth of fire. Michelle somehow managed to wrench her friend from Miss Sheldrake's grip, and pushed her into the relative safety of a corner.

Next, grotesque oversized bat-like creatures with foaming fanged mouths flew screeching out of the hole in the floor and started to attack the two girls. Then Julie felt something heavy crawling on her back and turned to see a giant furry moth with a terrifying face gazing at her with a pair of black domed eyes. Its unnaturally long spiral tongue coiled and uncoiled, each time flicking against her cheek and making her shudder with revulsion. Michelle came to her rescue yet again and punched the creature in the face, sending it flying. It landed on a bookshelf in a cloud of gold-brown dust.

"Julie, listen to me," and she slapped the face of her crying friend and kept on telling her, "None of this is real, just close your eyes and it'll all go away," and finally the girl did. "Sing this hymn with me, okay?" Michelle told her, and embraced her friend and launched into Ave Maria at the top of her voice.

Julie joined in the hymn, and although she didn't know the Latin words, she certainly knew the melody, and amidst the dreadful wails and moans still coming from the hole, the girls bravely sang the hymn dedicated to the Blessed Virgin Mary.

Within seconds, the ferocious heat in the classroom was no more, and when the girls opened their eyes, they saw that Laura Sheldrake was slumped across her desk, groaning in agony. She had been drained both physically and mentally by the sheer concentration needed to conjure up the illusion of Hell, and the Ave Maria had evidently cancelled out her remaining dark powers. Her hair was grey once again and her face was sullen-skinned and as wrinkled as a deflated balloon. She cast an unnerving wide globular eye at the girls and summoning the last of her energy, she hissed at them venomously.

Michelle flung open the door of the classroom, and she and Julie raced down the corridor – straight into the arms of the headmaster Mr O'Shaugnessy. He demanded to know why they had caused their classmates to stampede out of the art room. Normally respectful of their teachers and in awe of their headmaster, the girls ignored him and fought to get past him, only too aware that they were not yet out of danger. They heard a noise behind them, and turned to see an old hag with white hair and a stoop, but wearing the clothes of Laura Sheldrake.

"Who's on earth's that?" said Mr O'Shaugnessy, failing to recognise his art teacher, and he suddenly froze, statue-like, as the witch pointed her crooked finger at him. Julie and Michelle ran off down the corridor and into the gymnasium, where two classes were playing volleyball. The duo panted up to Mr Phillips, the PE teacher and tried to explain to him what was happening, but he was not prepared to listen to their gibberings about a witch and demons and a vision of Hell. He was furious with Michelle and Julie for disrupting the games and his lesson and told them to report to the headmaster immediately.

The double doors of the gymnasium suddenly crashed open and the dreaded Miss Sheldrake hobbled in, screaming and cursing Michelle and Julie for prematurely ageing her. Consumed with rage, she pointed her long bony finger at Michelle, upon which something unseen whistled through the air and slammed into the girl with a tremendous force, flinging her against the wall bars and knocking her clean out.

The malevolent witch then closed in on Julie, who was kneeling beside her unconscious friend, trying to bring her round. The witch's face was now so heavily wrinkled that it bore virtually no resemblance to the thirty-one-year-old art teacher Laura Sheldrake, so the PE teacher Mr Phillips and the girls of the two volleyball classes wondered who she could possibly be.

"Michelle, wake up! Please wake up," said Julie, repeatedly shaking her best friend, but the girl was still out cold.

"What on earth's going on here?" said Mr Phillips as he knelt down beside Michelle and examined her.

Julie had gone beyond fear and was furious at what Miss Sheldrake had done. She remembered what Michelle had said about combating an evil witch – she must be publicly accused in front of as many people as possible. Julie calmly stood up and pointed her finger at the decrepit old woman who was staggering towards her and loudly announced: "I accuse you, Laura Sheldrake, of being a witch! I accuse you! I accuse you of consorting with the Devil!"

Miss Sheldrake let out an agonised scream, and turned away from her accuser. She shuffled away, and Julie was ready to follow with the two classes of pupils whom she was rallying to the cause. Mr Phillips told her to be quiet but he could see her distress from the tears in her eyes. She thought Michelle was dead. The witch left the gymnasium, and the doors locked themselves behind her for almost a minute. By the time Julie and two other girls had managed to wrench open those doors, the evil Miss Sheldrake had gone. Michelle was then taken to the medical room where she was examined by the school nurse and later sent home to recover from concussion.

Laura Sheldrake was never heard from again, and her sudden disappearance was reported in the local press.

Three days after the showdown with Miss Sheldrake, Julie's grandmother, Peggy, called the two girls over to her house, telling them that she had something very important to tell them. After listening to the account of their ordeal, she revealed an amazing secret: she was the head witch of a local coven. Michelle suddenly remembered having seen her that terrible evening in her bedroom, when Miss Sheldrake had unleashed so much supernatural havoc and she understood that it was she who had saved her.

"Wow, Gran! That's amazing!"

"All in a day's work for a witch, love," said Michelle's gran, with a smile. "And you two are invited to join my coven." Michelle and Julie, sitting on the fireside rug at her feet, were barely able to contain their excitement. "Michelle, you have read a great deal about Wicca," continued Peggy. "Do you remember the Wiccan Rede?" Michelle nodded, and slowly recited the creed of all Wiccans. "Very good," said Peggy, and added, "you'll both be good witches in a year and a day. I'll guide you as best I can."

"Nan," said Julie, gazing in awe at her grandmother, "I always knew you were something very special – this explains everything."

Peggy smiled and stroked her head and Julie asked if her Michelle's mum was also a witch.

"No she isn't, and she certainly mustn't know about any of this."

"What happened to Miss Sheldrake?" asked Michelle.

Peggy gazed into the flames of the fire with so much wisdom in her eyes.

"Unfortunately, she's still about, disguised as an even younger woman now, a teenager in fact. Believe it or not, she's over two centuries old."

Both girls gasped and looked at each other.

"Yes, that's right, two hundred years old," Peggy assured her young listeners, and warned them that they would undoubtedly meet Miss Sheldrake again. "Her real name's Alice Stroud, and our three paths will almost certainly cross hers again one day."

Peggy also explained how the covens of good witches protected everyday non-Wiccan people from such witches as Alice, and she revealed that Miss Finnegan was a member of a 'White Light' coven based in Sefton.

"Will Miss Finnegan use her powers to make Mr Fenn fall in love with her, Nan?" asked Julie, with the fire glinting in her mischievous eye.

"I don't think so," replied Peggy, "It's wrong to force a person to love you. I think Mr Fenn is already fond of Kate Finnegan anyway. Love has a magic all of its own."

STRANGE BIRD OF PASSAGE

Flinders Street is no more, but back in the late nineteenth century it was a busy Kirkdale thoroughfare that ran from Commercial Road to Stanley Road, and in the year 1897, a rather suspicious-looking gentleman called at one of the lodging houses on this street. He was of middling size, and he wore a long full-length tweed-wool frock coat and a black slouch hat, and he carried an old scuffed oversized portmanteau case.

The lodging house, at Number 79 Flinders Street, was run by a world-weary Irish Liverpool man named Joe Turner, and from the moment he set eyes on the lodger, he thought there was something sinister about him. The stranger signed his name in the lodging house register as Mr Jones, but people in the area believed he was a Lithuanian, as he had been heard speaking in that language by Mr Isaacs, a local Russian-born grocer. Jones had a long prominent aquiline nose, a small bald head with tufts of hair above the ears, and a striking stoop, as if he'd been accustomed to crouching in his occupation and he'd stuck like that. Perhaps he was a clerk or a writer.

Mr Jones demanded, and was given, the attic lodgings as advertised in the window, and paid for a fortnight's stay in advance. Joe Turner's nine-year-old nephew, Paddy, lugged the new lodger's heavy oblong-shaped portmanteau up the six flights of stairs – and received only a nod and a smile from Jones in return. Then the door was slammed in his face.

Very strange things happened in the city that week, and only young Paddy had the brains and the intuition to connect them to the mysterious Mr Jones, but nobody was prepared to listen to his conclusions.

One late afternoon, an enormous black bird, resembling a raven, but with an estimated wingspan of some twelve feet, was seen in flight over the Huskisson Branch Dock. Stevedores and merchants, who shared a suspicious nature with their seafaring counterparts, regarded the bird as a bad omen. One sea captain, who had recently returned from San Francisco, believed the creature to be an imported Californian condor – a giant South American bird with a nine-foot wingspan, although it was known that such birds had a bald yellow head, and the ominous bird wheeling above them had a black head.

Everyone on the quayside, and people on the waterfront's Regent Road, stood spellbound, watching the giant bird as it circled above them and occasionally plunged down to the banks of the river. It flew towards the east, and cast a gargantuan shadow over Stanley Park, where it was seen to dive and seize something. Some witnesses claimed that it was a small child, but the general consensus was that a dog had been picked up by the talons of the enormous bird. The rumours of the giant bird swept the city, and most intelligent people dismissed the weird story as superstitious nonsense.

However, two days later, at 5.30am, Mr Jones crept from his room carrying a hessian sack and went down into the backyard to empty its contents into the dustbin. Paddy was awakened by the creaking of the stairs and peeped out of his bedroom window. He saw him carefully covering the refuse with newspapers and instantly became suspicious, so he later went down to have a look in the bin. What he saw chilled him to his marrow. Under the crumpled papers he found several fish heads – as well as the skeletal remains of a small dog ...

"You're talking daft now, Paddy," landlord Joe Turner told his nine-year-old nephew when the lad told him what he'd seen and claimed that Mr Jones, the new lodger up in the garret, had dumped the remains after his 'giant bird' had eaten the flesh.

"And where exactly would he be keeping this giant bird?" Joe asked young Paddy, whilst lighting his pipe.

"In Mr Jones's big case, of course, Uncle Joe!" the child replied. "That'll be why it was so heavy."

Joe smirked and patronisingly patted the child's head, but the conversation with his nephew had turned his mind to his enigmatic new lodger. He leaned on the mantelpiece in the front parlour, thinking about Mr Jones, and how he always went out to eat – and never even came down for breakfast. Perhaps he had to eat kosher food, or was on some other special diet, the landlord reasoned. Out of curiosity he went into the backyard and examined the dustbin – and to his utter horror he found the six fish heads and the stinking carcass of an animal, just as Paddy had described. On closer examination he saw that the animal was a young mongrel dog. Joe recoiled with a handkerchief to his mouth. Of course, he did not believe for one minute that any bird had eaten that dog, but perhaps some 'heathen' from Lithuania, where dogs were perhaps considered to be a delicacy ...

Whatever the explanation, Joe wanted to get to the bottom of the grisly

39

remains and so he climbed the sixty steps up to the garret to have words with Mr Jones but there was no answer when he knocked and when he tried the handle, he found that the door was locked from the inside.

"I know you're in there, Mr Jones!" shouted the landlord through the keyhole. "So you might as well come out now."

This finally elicited a response; the lodger shouted something back in his foreign tongue and threw an object at the door. This was not the reaction that Joe Turner was expecting. He had had some very strange lodgers in his time, but this fellow was in a class of his own! He went back down to the parlour and apologised to his nephew for doubting his story. Paddy looked up from cleaning out the ashes from the fireplace.

"I told you he was creepy, didn't I, Uncle Joe," he said, wide-eyed, kneeling on the newspapers which he'd spread across the hearth rug. "It must be a pretty big bird to pick a dog up and eat it like that," said the boy, lost in morbid contemplation.

"Listen, son," said Joe. "I'm telling you once and for all, no bird ate that dog," and he shook his head dismissively. "It's that lunatic upstairs who ate that dog. They've obviously got very peculiar tastes in food where he comes from. They'll eat anything"

"Uncle, where is Lithuania?" Paddy inquired.

His uncle, who hadn't got the faintest idea where it was, simulated a long coughing fit after puffing on his pipe, in order to evade the question. Eventually he stopped and said, by way of diversion. "Mind you don't get any of that ash on that rug."

"You know I'm always careful, Uncle."

Uncle Joe then warned his nephew not to go anywhere near the Lithuanian, saying that he could get into real trouble by poking his nose into things he didn't understand. But Paddy was not to be fobbed off. He was now even more convinced that their strange lodger was up to no good and he intended to discover exactly what was going on.

That evening, as Uncle Joe was snoring under a newspaper slumped in his fireside armchair, Paddy crept back upstairs to the garret, and peeped through the keyhole of Mr Jones's room. The room was bathed in the reddish gold light of a setting sun, and the garret window was wide open. At first, Paddy couldn't see or hear anything and thought he may have gone out. But then he nearly jumped out of his skin when he suddenly heard the lodger crying out. He uttered a succession of unfamiliar words and then made a dreadful inhuman rattling sound which seemed to resonate from deep down in the back of his throat, as if he were choking. There then followed a tense period of silence during which Paddy scarcely dared breathe, terrified lest he should be discovered by the creepy lodger.

What he saw next froze him to the very depths of his soul with fear. A giant black bird waddled into view, blocking out the sun's dying rays, and Paddy blinked through the keyhole in total disbelief. Its great claws rasped on the floorboards as the six foot tall bird struggled to manoeuvre itself in the cramped surroundings. The freaky creature had a man's head, but with the incongruous addition of a huge beak at the front – and a startlingly bald head. It had the head of Mr Jones! Somehow that bird was Mr Jones! By some sort of devilry the lodger had metamorphosed into this grotesque hybrid with feathers and fur covering his round chest from the neck down. Mr Jones's hands had been transformed into the talons of a bird, and he was now perched at the open window, ready to fly off.

Paddy couldn't suppress a small gasp of fright as the bird flexed its enormous wings, and it was alerted immediately. It cocked its mighty head to one side, all its senses primed. Then it turned its head through one hundred and eighty degrees and the lens of its huge domed eye zoomed right into Paddy's eye at the keyhole. In a flash it hopped down off its perch and flew in a frenzy of fur and feathers at the door, its great beak smashing repeatedly through the wooden panels, as if they were matchwood …

Paddy's terrified screams echoed down the stairways of the house where they reached the ears of the slumbering Joe Turner. He woke up with a start and fought his way from under the newspaper before flying out of the front parlour to the foot of the stairs. He looked up the stairs to the source of the screams and heard his nephew's footfalls clattering towards him.

"Whatever's wrong, Paddy?" he asked, as the lad reached the first floor landing and he began to climb the stairs towards him, but Paddy came hurtling straight past his uncle and bolted into the parlour, where he disappeared under a table. Joe crouched down beneath the table and could plainly see that the child was trembling uncontrollably from head to foot.

"Paddy, what's wrong with you?" he asked, sternly. "I can't help you if you won't tell me what's wrong. You've not been up to see that foreign chap again, have you?"

As the boy's breathing gradually slowed, he managed to give a garbled account of his encounter with Mr Jones and of his incredible metamorphosis into the huge bird, and he quivered when he described how the unholy creature had gone for him and smashed great holes in the door. Joe had heard enough. He marched straight over to the sideboard, pulled out an old biscuit tin, lifted the lid, and took out a loaded revolver, then set off to confront whatever it was up there in the garret.

He could see where something had torn jagged holes in the attic door, just as Paddy had described, but peeping through them, Joe could see no signs of either the Lithuanian lodger, or of any giant bird. Holding the revolver out in front of him, he unlocked the door with his master key and cautiously entered the room. The garret windows were still wide open, and a brisk breeze from the river had chilled the room. Joe closed the windows and lit the gas mantle. He jumped when he heard the floorboard creak outside the door, but it was just young Paddy. He had conjured up enough courage to come out from under the table and was now determined to help his uncle fight that grotesque bird of terror.

"Go back downstairs, Paddy," his uncle told him, as his eyes took in the lodger's shirt, waistcoat, trousers and long-johns lying on the bed.

Paddy stayed put, wiping tears from his reddened eyes.

"But, Uncle I ..." he began, when the room suddenly darkened as something hovered outside the windows. It started to thump against the window panes, startling them both. Joe raised the revolver and aimed it straight at the casements, which were now bulging inwards, threatening to give way at any moment. He backed away towards the doorway, where Paddy was crying again. Then with a sudden roar, the windows burst open, and shards of glass and splintered frame showered the garret. Joe Turner froze with fear. An enormous black bird with a vaguely human beaked head squeezed through the window and entered the room – with something writhing frantically in its mouth.

The tip of each extended wing touched the walls on either side of the room – a span of at least fifteen feet. The unfortunate cat – for that was what it was – which was trapped in the monster's beak, was torn to shreds by two great claw-like hands, and the bird was so engrossed in its feeding frenzy that it didn't notice Joe Turner, and, mute with terror, he stepped behind the damaged door and closed it over. He took several deep breaths and then opened the door again and aimed the revolver straight at the bird. Its head twisted to face him and it let out a blood-curdling squawk as the landlord discharged six shots into it in quick succession. The bird screeched horribly and lunged at him, but Joe turned and ran, pushing Paddy ahead of him as he did so.

Uncle and nephew tumbled down the stairs with the nightmarish bird from Hell waddling obscenely after them. When Paddy picked himself up on the next landing, he saw his uncle groaning and clutching his knee. Halfway up the stairs lay the stunned bird with a glazed look in its eyes. Joe Turner scrambled painfully to his feet and cautiously approached the bird to have a closer look – upon which the bird suddenly became animated and batted him with its wing and raised its head, emitting a high-pitched cry which must have been heard for miles around. Joe was sent crashing through the banister and rails and fell on to the next flight of stairs in a senseless heap. The giant bird then seemed to summon all of its remaining strength and it slowly raised itself up. Having done so, it then steadily began to hobble down the stairs towards Paddy …

Paddy screamed out to his uncle, who was lying motionless among the splintered handrail and balusters on the descending flight of stairs. "Help me! Help me!" he yelled. The grotesque wounded bird hopped awkwardly down the stairs, limping and tilting its head to look at him side-on with its domed red-iris eyes. The boy decided to take a chance, and racing past it, picked up a length of the broken baluster and started taking swipes at the creature, aiming at its head. The bird shrieked like a stuck pig and desperately tried to extend its wings to shield itself from the blows raining down on its bald head. But so enormous was the bird, that it was hemmed in between the wall and the stairway rail and couldn't manoeuvre itself properly in the tight space. Paddy couldn't believe it when, unable to defend itself, he saw it slowly turn and limp back up to the garret, leaving him sobbing over his injured uncle.

Joe Turner soon regained consciousness, but before he and Paddy had a chance to discuss what to do next, they heard a knock at the front door. Joe groggily staggered downstairs with his nephew and opened the door to find an old man wearing a long black coat and a homburg hat. The man introduced himself as a Mr Steiner, and said that he'd observed the giant bird flying to and from the garret, and what's more, he claimed that he knew precisely who the 'bird-man' was. Most astonishing of all, he also claimed that he could kill him. There was something open and honest about the old foreign-sounding man, despite his wild claims, so, somewhat apprehensively, Joe decided to admit him into the house. Perhaps he really could help rid them of the avian menace.

Having accepted the drink that he was offered, the stranger proceeded to tell

Joe and Paddy a very unsettling story.

In broken English, Steiner told how, in the twelfth century, a snowstorm, almost unprecedented in its severity, had almost buried a Lithuanian village near Vilnius. The fallen snow quickly turned to ice and refused to thaw for months, and during the long freeze, the villagers were unable to get out to look for food. After having eaten all their winter preserves and grain as well as every animal within the confines of the village, the villagers were staring starvation in the face. They were almost ready to resort to cannibalism, when a strange gigantic bird suddenly landed in their midst. It had been seen around the region for many years and was said to be the embodiment of an evil magician who had been transformed into a bird a hundred years before, as punishment for inflicting terrible atrocities on the people of the region.

Now, to the starving villagers the bird meant only one thing: food. It was soon shot and stoned and then lassoed. However, the bird did not finish up in the communal cooking pot. Instead, a prominent local family used brute force to claim the creature as their own, and it was promptly roasted on their spit, filling the whole village with delicious aromas, which nearly drove the famished villagers mad. A holy man warned the family against consuming the bird's flesh, predicting that they would all be cursed as a result and in time would themselves change into such a bird. The ravenous family listened impatiently to his warnings but ate the bird anyway.

The snows eventually thawed and spring arrived. Most of the villagers had survived the great hunger, but the people of the castle were not so lucky, and they slowly began to turn into giant birds; birds with an unholy appetite for human flesh. They fed off the hapless villagers for many years despite them trying everything to defend themselves. Eventually it was discovered that the creatures could be killed by using silver-tipped arrows and so the cull began. But some of the giant birds escaped, and underwent a secondary metamorphosis, becoming human again for a while. Mr Jones was the last descendant of this cursed clan. Steiner had followed him all the way to Liverpool – and was now ready to kill him and so put an end to the curse. The old man produced a gun, explaining that it had silver-tipped bullets in its chamber. He then climbed up to the garret, accompanied by Joe Turner and Paddy.

They found Jones still partially transformed into the devil bird. Without hesitation, Steiner shot him three times through the heart. The tormented feathered figure toppled backwards out of the garret window, but somehow managed to cling to the window frame with its claws. Steiner held out his hand, and a gnarled clawed hand weakly grasped his palm. The old man then pulled the partially transformed creature back into the room, where it collapsed on the floor and died. Before their eyes the corpse slowly changed fully back into a man again, before disintegrating into a pile of grey dust.

Until his death in the late 1950s, Paddy Turner told anyone who would listen about this strange incident, and swore that it had really happened. Who knows? Perhaps Shakespeare was right; maybe there really are more things in heaven and earth than are dreamt of in our philosophy.

THE SUNDAY KING

Once upon a time, one wet summer Sunday afternoon in the 1950s, three children in Wavertree named Violet, Charlie and Jimmy – all aged thirteen – were climbing the walls with boredom at a house in Arnold Grove. The three of them hated Sundays, they were always like this. In an attempt to amuse them, Violet's Auntie Ivy lifted the lid of the upright piano and coaxed angel-voiced Jimmy to sing a popular song of the day called 'You Belong to Me', but Rebel, Charlie's over-fed dinosaur of a Labrador dog, began to howl alongside. Auntie Ivy slammed the piano lid shut and scolded the skulking dog.

"Go home then misery chops!" she told him, and stormed off into the kitchen to finish peeling the potatoes.

"Come on then, Rebel," said Charlie, tapping his dog's head and walking towards the door, "I don't think we're welcome here any more," he said melodramatically.

Violet told him to stop being so silly and she and Jimmy followed him out into the dead-end-street. The unappetising aromas of boiled cabbage and cauliflower hung in the air as the women of Arnold Grove prepared their Sunday dinners. The rain had stopped at last, and the three teens and the galumphing dog wandered off with no particular place to go – anything was better than being stuck in the house. As they passed through Childwall, the sun broke through at last, and the grey spaces in the heavens were transformed into a glorious summer-blue, and swallows twittered on high.

Slick-quiffed Simon Lee, one of the first Teddy Boys in Liverpool, sauntered up from the direction of Jackson's Pond in a chequered shirt, tight jeans and crepe-soled shoes. He always walked around like he owned the place. Violet blushed bright red as soon as she saw him and bowed her head.

"Hey, Vi, here's your fellah," laughed Charlie, turning to tell his friend, and, seeing she'd changed colour, he mocked her coyness. "Ha! Vi's gone like a beetroot! Look at her!"

The eighteen-year-old Teddy Boy padded silently past on his suede crepe-soled shoes, completely unaware that the girl passing by had the most terrible crush on him and had burst into tears when she had seen him walking with the beautiful Crow twins to Capaldi's Milk Bar. How could he be so blind as to not to notice me? Violet thought longingly, turning to watch him walk away under the dappled green shades of Childwall's trees. Jimmy was much more sympathetic than Charlie about Violet's unrequited love, for he was in love with a girl who served in a local cake shop and he yearned to ask her out, but was simply too shy. Jimmy gave a knowing smile to Violet and she smiled back, fighting back the tears. Then Charlie suddenly bolted off, trying to leave his dog behind, but Rebel yelped and bounded after him.

At around three o'clock that afternoon, the trio were standing before the giant floral Cuckoo Clock in Woolton's Walled Garden, in the middle of the woods. Erratic but graceful butterflies with fiery red wings fluttered about the multi-coloured flowers on the face of the clock, and Charlie tried to hit one of them with a stone from his catapult, but struck the minute-hand instead, making a loud pinging sound, upon which the park keeper told him off. Charlie hurled a cheeky remark and the 'parky' chased him and Violet and Jimmy out of the walled garden and towards Camp Hill.

The young teenagers managed to make their escape from the parkeeper, who soon gave up the chase, but then found themselves faced with a very peculiar sight in the middle of the nearby woods, for seated on a throne in the middle of a clearing, they came upon a bearded man wearing a gold crown, decked out in luxurious robes of scarlet and ermine. Minstrels with lutes were singing before him, and an odd-looking jester with wings on either wide of his head, was laughing and pointing at the three startled youths. Suddenly, Violet felt a heavy gauntleted hand on her shoulder, and turned to see a gaunt-faced giant of a man wearing a chain-mail balaclava and armour.

Another soldier grabbed hold of Jimmy, but wily Charlie managed to avoid being caught and ran off, scared out of his wits, with Rebel following close behind. The youth and his dog ran all the way to the home of Violet's Auntie Ivy at Arnold Grove. Ivy and a local Wavertree policeman, PC Thompson, all rushed off to Camp Hill, where they made a thorough search of the woods, accompanied by Charlie and Rebel, but they could find no trace of either Violet or Jimmy. Additional policemen and several local people joined in the search, which carried on after dark.

At around midnight, something bizarre happened – Violet and Jimmy seemed to appear out of nowhere at the crest of Camp Hill, giving a group of searchers a fright. When the two anxious-looking teens explained where they'd been for the last nine hours, PC Thompson accused them of wasting police time, and Auntie Ivy was furious.

"Is this your idea of a joke?" she hissed. "Just wait till I get you home, you silly pair. I've been frantic with worry about you,"

Between sobs, Violet told her how she and Jimmy had been prisoners of the 'Sunday King', a vagrant who had given his soul to the Devil in order to become a king, but the Devil, being a trickster, had taken the tramp's soul but merely made him a king for one day each week – Sunday. The rest of the week he was reduced to being a poor vagrant. King Gardyloo, as he was named, had in turn tricked other down-and-outs into selling their souls in order to become members of his royal court. The jester, Mugwort, the minstrels, and all other courtiers all lived extravagantly every Sunday in a secret palace under the summit of Camp Hill. King Gardyloo had tried to persuade Violet to become his queen but she had rejected his offer outright, even though Mugwort the jester had threatened to tickle her until she agreed to the bargain. The, at midnight, the King and his retinue of courtiers had turned into down-and-outs once more, and the palace, and all its trappings, had vanished.

Of course, Violet and Jimmy were not believed, but, of course, Charlie had also seen King Gardyloo, Mugwort, the minstrels and soldiers, and on the following Saturday, he was walking down Woolton Road when he noticed seven tramps standing by the lodge house of Bishop Eton Church. A kindly priest was handing out sandwiches and cups of tea to a long line of vagrants. One of them had fine thick hair of a lustrous gold colour, and he turned to look at Charlie. The boy noticed the tramp's regal-looking face and bearing and realised at once that it was the uncrowned King Gardyloo! The mischievous-looking unfortunate standing next to him grinned, and Charlie instantly recognised him as Mugwort the jester. Three nearby giant vagrants in grimy clothes were obviously the king's fearsome soldiers, minus their armour and chain-mail. The other two discards of humanity were easily identifiable as the minstrels.

Charlie ran back to Arnold Grove and told Violet and Jimmy about the tramps and from that time onwards, the children would visit Camp Hill every Sunday in order to catch a glimpse of the Sunday King and his courtiers.

Violet, Jimmy and Charlie are still around today, all now in their sixties, and they are adamant that the Sunday King of Camp Hill did exist, but that no one knows what eventually became of him and his courtiers. Some say a nun battled with the Devil to get the souls of the vagrants back, whereas some believe that King Gardyloo still reigns each Sunday at Camp Hill.

Indeed, Camp Hill is something of a haunted hot-spot, and many strange apparitions have been seen there over the years. A ghostly tent often materialises among the woods on Camp Hill, and strange silhouetted figures can be seen moving about within it. Below the summit of Camp Hill, an ancient Iron Age fort is said to still be buried, and an eerie glow has often been reported in the woods there; it may be nothing more than the Willo-o'-the-wisp, or it could be something genuinely paranormal.

THE TARBOCK FIEND

The Brick Wall Inn is a pub that stands on Netherley Road, Tarbock, on the outskirts of Liverpool. It was built in 1940 on the site of the original inn of the same name, which was built in the late seventeenth century, and although the inn today still has its own collection of innocuous ghosts (as do most pubs), the area in which it is set was once the backdrop of a terrifying supernatural mystery.

The creature was known as the 'Tarbock Fiend', or the 'Cronton Vampire' and by many another name as well, but to this day no one knows just exactly what instilled so much fear into the hearts of the people who lived in the countryside surrounding the Brick Wall Inn all those years ago.

Around 1838, a group of farmers formed the Farmers Rest Lodge, a friendly society that acted both as a co-operative group and a charity for worthy causes. The lodge met at the Brick Wall Inn, and one blazing July day in 1839, as the farmers converged on the meeting place, two of them came across an injured girl of about fourteen years of age, crying inconsolably as she staggered along a cinder track that is now Greensbridge Lane. The girl was clutching her neck which was soaked in blood, and further down the road her frightened horse was seized. The whites of the terrified animal's eyes could be seen and, its nostrils flared and its ears were pinned back. It was quivering with fear and bore the marks of what seemed like a savage knife-attack.

The farmers tried to ascertain what had happened to the girl and as her sobs died down she gave a garbled description of her attacker. He was much much taller than herself, she said, muscular, and with a mass of unruly black hair and a beard. His nose was large and wide, and his mouth contained a row of half rotted fangs. His bulging eyes were crackling with insanity and he looked more like an animal than a human being. He wore a long flowing black cape and a pair of black leather gauntlets, and he had used his gloved hands to try and throttle the girl as he attacked her after jumping out from behind some trees as she rode along the lane. The brute had dragged the girl off her horse and bit into her neck. He ran off when she screamed and managed to wrestle herself out of his clutches and vanish into the nearby woods. The girl was taken to the Brick Wall Inn where her wounds were cleaned and bandaged by a local doctor.

The 'fiend' was seen mostly at night after that, and despite the attempts of a posse of armed farmers to track the beastly assailant down, he was never caught. There were reported sightings and attacks of the Tarbock Fiend across several manors, and he was sighted in places ranging from the land where Netherley now stands, right up to Cronton, where he was regarded as some kind of vampire. The fiend then seemed to go into hibernation for many years but returned with a vengeance in the 1840s.

At around this time, the cloaked figure of the Victorian bogeyman Spring-Heeled Jack was also seen in various parts of England, and some witnesses confused sightings of the caped fiend with Jack and vice versa. Eventually the fiend of Tarbock once again vanished into obscurity for a time, but then between 1898-59 – years after the initial attack – a rumour spread throughout an area bounded by Halewood, Tarbock and Knowsley which stated that the dreaded fiend had returned.

One stormy night in 1898, a local vagrant barged into the Brick Wall Inn, completely out of breath and in a state of abject terror. He told the pub landlord Jim Ambrose that the Devil had chased him across the fields. The tale the tramp told was so frighteningly convincing that the superstitious landlord locked the inn door and loaded his shotgun. Moments later, something pounded heavily at this door, and a grotesque spine-chilling face was spied gazing through a window. People refused to go home from the pub until almost four o'clock in the morning when the grey light of dawn crept over the manor.

Was the visitation nothing more than the work of a prankster? Was it all in the mind? If the attacks were the work of a real vampire, is it possible that the Tarbock Fiend still be around today?

THE CROXTETH WIND DEVIL

A sceptic once remarked to me that, he only believed what he could see, and I told him that we actually see represents less than a millionth of what is really there. The universe is infinite and our weak imperfect eyes can only detect the tiniest amount of it, because, on the cosmological scale, we are smaller than a virus. I pointed out to the sceptic that there is a familiar invisible force that demolishes buildings, knocks down people, uproots trees, stirs the sea into mountainous waves, and smashes ships against the rocks. We call it the wind, but who has ever seen this tremendous force, which whines, howls, whistles and roars around us? Like everyone else, I have never seen it, but I don't question that it exists.

Something mischievous and invisible that was initially blamed on the wind haunted two Croxteth women in 2005, but the entity displayed an intelligence as well as a rather vicious streak.

One afternoon, Jenny, a woman in her early twenties, set off to pick up her eleven-year-old child from Our Lady and St Swithin's primary school on Petherick Road, Croxteth. It was a calm sunny pleasant autumn day, and on her return journey she walked hand in hand with her child towards their home, which was approximately a quarter of a mile away. As mother and child were walking along, a miniature whirlwind spun a pile of leaves into a helix on the pavement ahead of them. These leaves didn't scatter, and the little 'twister' didn't dissipate – but instead began to trail after Jenny and her child, who giggled at the odd sight. The eerie whirlwind followed Jenny across a busy road, where it was seen by dozens of other people, before finally dying out on the road where Jenny lived. The young mother entered her home, sat her child down on the sofa to watch a *Dora the Explorer* cartoon, then went into the garden to take in the washing from the line.

As she was unpegging the washing, Jenny heard a rustle amongst the bushes separating her garden from next door's. A gust of wind blew past her and encircled her, sending her long hair straight upwards in a spiralling motion, almost plaiting the strands. With a growing feeling of unease, Jenny remembered the strange rotating column of air that had followed her from the school to the house. After a few moments, the whirlwind moved away from her and headed for the plastic washing basket laden with the dried washing. The clothes from the basket were thrown up into the air with such force that a tracksuit top landed on the roof of the garden shed. Jenny then watched, bewildered, as the sinister wind devil spun into the kitchen, throwing open the back door with enormous force. Jenny ran after it, fearing for her child's safety, and was horrified to see the invisible atmospheric disturbance scattering tea towels and oven gloves across the kitchen as it whistled and howled around the room. Next it moved off into the hallway, where a picture hanging on the wall was knocked crooked, and then the door leading to the lounge was blown open by the unearthly gust. Upon reaching the lounge, Jenny was relieved to see that the vortex had apparently blown itself out, but not before numerous sheets of A4 stationery paper on which her child had been drawing had been flung across the length of the room.

Jennifer phoned her friend Adele, who lived in the same street, and told her about the terrifying whirlwind and asked if she had experienced any similar problems. Her friend, who was highly sceptical about ghosts and the paranormal in general, answered that she had noticed nothing unusual and suggested that it had all probably been nothing more than the normal draughts that you get in the house, caused by the wind outside. However, three days later, the same spooky whirlwind invaded Adele's garden and home, terrifying her dog to such an extent that the animal cleared the back garden hedge and ended up cowering in a neighbour's dog kennel.

This atmospheric phenomenon has not been experienced since, and it is difficult to offer a rational explanation for it. Adele had the presence of mind to take a photograph capturing several items of her washing spiralling across her garden, and there are many so-called 'orbs' of blue and purple light in the snap. In the world of the supernatural, vortexes of spirit energy have been reported from time to time, but they are as mysterious and inexplicable as the Croxteth wind devil.

HEALING LIGHTS

Evening zephyrs murmured among the trees of Princes Park in that unforgettable summer of 1941. Parts of the city lay cratered and ruined in the aftermath of the May Blitz, and blackout curtains ensured that not a glimmer of light shone from any home as night fell on the Dingle and Toxteth. Six-year-old Miranda should have been sleeping soundly in her bed on the top floor of an old Victorian house on Devonshire Road, but instead she had mischievously pulled the blackout curtain aside and peeped out into the twilit heavens. High above the war-torn troubled world, all the stars were beginning to make their appearance, their full beauty made more apparent because of the blackout. Nowadays light pollution in our towns and cities has robbed us of this wonderful nightly spectacle.

Miranda was transfixed by the stars and tried to count them, but she was distracted by the beautiful golden light that beamed down from an enormous jewel of a star that she saw most nights. That star and its beautiful beam of light was, in the childish eyes of Miranda, a fairy; her special fairy. The light poured through the windowpane and she gasped in awe as the dazzling haloed orb glowed with its own heat-giving light, giving off so much warmth that it made Miranda's face turn pink. The 'fairy' slowly orbited the child and started to cast beams of strong blue light on to her right leg, which was withered with poliomyelitis. Young as she was, Miranda was only too aware that there was something wrong with that leg, and she hated the cumbersome leg-brace that she had to wear every day in order to be able to walk. It stopped her from running and playing like the other children and it was her greatest wish that the leg should be like all her friends'.

As soon as Miranda's mother, Gillian, came up the stairs to check on her daughter, the 'fairy' would always flit back through the window and soar up into the heavens. But each night the enchanting star would return, floating into the room and directing its warm beams on to the child's leg. Gradually that leg became stronger and better, until Miranda could walk properly again without the help of the loathsome leg-brace. She was taken to see a specialist who decided that the child could not have been stricken with polio in the first place after all.

It must have been some other unknown muscular condition, he deduced, because in no other way could he explain the miraculous cure of the affected limb. Miranda matter-of-factly told her mother that it was the fairy who had made her better, but, of course, she wasn't believed.

Then one evening that summer, Gillian's younger sister, Brenda, was taking the washing in from the backyard clothes line when she saw not one, but three of these fairies that her little niece Miranda had talked about so much. They floated silently over the backyard wall like luminous soap bubbles and circled the startled young woman. She was naturally alarmed at first, yet she found the beautiful colours of the radiant visitors so utterly mesmerising, that slowly she calmed herself down and was able to ask them, "Are you fairies?"

Beams of sky-blue light shone from two of the sparkling orbs and scanned Brenda's face and shoulders. The young woman reached out to touch one of the shimmering etheric globes but it retreated over the wall in a flash, quickly followed by the others.

Not long afterwards, Brenda realised that a nagging toothache which she had had for weeks had stopped from the time of the encounter with the floating lights, and it never returned. The lights were never seen again, but Brenda, Gillian and little Miranda often spoke about them and wished that they would return. Were they really fairies, or visitors from another world? We may discover more about them one day.

THE SEVEN WHISTLERS

The maisonettes stood on Mason Street, Edge Hill; a street now synonymous with the enigmatic tunnels excavated below its sandstone bedrock, carved out long ago by the workforce of the so-called 'Mad Mole', Joseph Williamson, but this eerie tale does not concern him – it concerns a dark legend of sky-born death-bringers, and some say that it is a legend best left forgotten. However, as you well know, I see it as my job to delve into Liverpool's dark forgotten legends, and so I bring the tale of the Seven Whistlers to your attention, and if by some unfortunate chance you should happen to hear them, I sincerely apologise in advance, but it will have been your curiosity that will have led you to hear their ominous pipes.

But let me give you one final chance to avoid them: skip this chapter and instead read one of the other strange tales in this book, because if you read on, you just might find that your ears and your mind are unusually receptive to their deadly callings in the hush after sunset, or in the coffin silence of the dead of night. For many of the people to whom I have told this tale, have subsequently heard the Whistlers – end of warning!

Well, and now back to the maisonettes on Mason Street. It all began on a Thursday evening, in late July, 1979, at around 9.30pm. Twenty-six-year-old Denise was sitting on a sofa, smoking a Players cigarette as she settled down to watch a sitcom called *Shelley*, while her boyfriend Martin was out in the kitchen, pouring out two cups of tea as he monitored the cheese on toast he had prepared bubbling under the grill. The sun had already gone down and had left a sky of faded gold in its wake. Incandescent fiery spurs of orange cloud drifted in the darkness creeping down through the sky as night began its reign.

Martin came into the living room carrying the smaller plate of cheese on toast first and placed it on a cheap little rickety-legged coffee table with a wood-effect surface. Denise wasn't hungry and waved it away rather ungraciously, "You have it", she said, squinting as her cigarette smoke stung her eye and she took another drag. "I've lost my appetite."

"Probably by smoking too many of those things," said Martin, shaking his head.

He returned to the kitchen for the two mugs of tea and his own cheese on toast. He started to tuck into the toast as a commercial break interrupted the programme, and Denise's eyes wandered away from the television towards the glowing crimson sky.

"What the heck was that?" she suddenly said.

Remote controls for televisions were rare in those days, and so she got up from the sofa and turned the volume control down on the old Pye television set – and listened.

"What?" said Martin, his cheek bulging with toast and cheese. "I didn't hear a thing."

"Shush!" Denise told him, and looked down at the window sill as she listened intently.

Martin could still hear nothing.

"That wasn't half weird," said Denise.

"What was?" said Martin, still munching. "What the heck are you going on about? Come and eat your cheese on toast before it gets cold. You're always wasting food."

Denise opened the window, and seeing that no one was about on Mason Street, she flicked the burnt-down stub of her cigarette down on to the pavement below.

"It was a sort of screeching whistling sound," she said. "I can't really describe it."

"Crosvilles probably," said Martin, and got up off the sofa to turn the television volume up.

"You what?" Denise turned and grimaced, as she didn't understand what he was talking about.

"You probably heard the brakes of one of those Crosville buses. They make a whistling screeching sound," said Martin, without taking his eyes of the telly.

Denise turned back to the window, "Oh, it couldn't have been a bus. It was really loud. Didn't you hear it?"

"No," said Martin firmly, obviously finding the whole business very tiresome. He was about to stretch out to make himself more comfortable on the sofa when there was a knock at the door. "Who's that?' he said, irritated, hoping it wasn't Carol, one of Denise's many over-talkative friends.

"If it's Carol tell her I'm not in, and if it's Cathy say I'm in bed and not well, I owe her a few bob," whispered Denise.

Martin went to the door, but soon returned with a worried look on his face.

"It's some weird gypsy woman, and I can't get rid of her," he whispered.

"What? Oh, let me go," said Denise impatiently. " I'll soon get rid of her, just you watch."

Denise brushed past him and went to the front door. A tall woman in her late forties, or early fifties, dressed all in black and with a head of tight black curly hair, stood on the doorstep. She certainly looked intimidating; her face was sullen, almost angry, and her nose was long and broad. Her dark brown eyes were large and protruded abnormally, producing a permanent stare. She held a small bag in her hand, and when she saw Denise, she grinned, revealing a set of large square teeth. The grin did nothing to improve her sullen appearance.

"Hello, love," she said in a gravelly, almost masculine voice, "Do you want to buy some pegs?"

"No thanks," said Denise, and she put her hand on the knob of the Yale door-lock.

"Or lucky stones?" persisted the woman.

"No thank you," Denise told her sternly.

From the moment she had set eyes on the caller she had felt there was something spooky about her.

Then all of a sudden, Denise heard the strange whistling sound that she had heard briefly earlier on. She tried to determine who, or what, was making the sounds, and she decided that it must be a group of people whistling random notes, though for what reason she couldn't imagine.

The 'gypsy' woman heard the whistling too, and her large eyes darted anxiously about and became full of concern as the whistling echoed along the landing. Without warning, the woman suddenly let out an horrendous scream that brought Martin bounding to the front door. He swore loudly and asked what was going on, and the woman threw her hands up to her face and started to shudder violently.

"What's wrong with you?" Denise asked, feeling both angry and yet scared by the woman's bizarre antics.

"The Seven Whistlers," said the woman in black. "They're about."

An unpleasant cold sensation tingled from the top to the bottom of Denise's spine. She turned to Martin, who was looking at the twilight caller with an expression of unbridled annoyance.

"Can you hear that noise now?" asked Denise.

This time, Martin could hear the weird whistling, but he was more concerned about getting rid of the gypsy.

"Haven't heard from them for years," wailed the woman, and then ran off along the landing, long skirts flying, before they could extract any more information out of her.

Denise slammed and bolted the door and and went back into the living room, all the time thinking about their visitor's mysterious words. What did she mean by the Seven Whistlers? She shuddered violently, her body going into a peculiar spasm which Martin noticed immediately. He asked her what the matter was.

"Someone just walked over my grave," was Denise's unsettling reply.

She lit another cigarette and smoked it nervously. She was aware that *News At Ten* was starting on the television but she couldn't concentrate properly on what the newsreader was saying. She decided that she would go and visit her mother and talk it over with her, and so she told Martin her intentions, promising to be back at around half-past eleven. Martin was very reluctant to let her go; he didn't like her going out on her own at night at the best of times, never mind when there were strange women hanging about. He told her to be careful coming home from her mum's at that time of night, then he kissed her, and sat down to watch the news and the late-night film, even though, like Denise, he couldn't really concentrate on what he was watching.

Denise walked quickly to her mother's home on Sheil Road, looking behind herself with every few steps. As usual, she received a very warm welcome. Her mum was doing the ironing and her grandmother was sitting at the table in the kitchen, with the radio on low in the background. They'd been reminiscing about old times, and Denise's gran was sipping a half-pint glass of stout, which she did every evening at about the same time. Denise's mum made her daughter a strong mug of tea and plonked down a plate of assorted biscuits on the chequered tablecloth.

"I knew you'd come here tonight, our Denise," said her gran. "I just knew somehow."

Denise smiled and then told the two of them about the strange incident that had happened earlier at the maisonette.

"That's funny, isn't it? Sure it wasn't seagulls you heard?" was all her mother could say.

"No, mum, it was nothing like seagulls," said Denise, rolling her eyes in annoyance. "You're as bad as Martin! It was like loads of people, all whistling at the same time. And then that gypsy woman goes and says something about the Seven Whistlers, whoever they are. I wonder what she could have meant? It really creeped me out."

"Do you and Martin still go to church?" Denise's grandmother suddenly asked.

"No, we haven't been for months," Denise said, and then started to worry at her gran's words. She was a fount of supernatural tales and information, and could interpret dreams, omens and signs. "Why? What's that got to do with anything, gran?"

"Oh … nothing," said the old woman mysteriously. She continued sipping her stout and looked up to see two curious female faces. Denise and her mother were desperate to know what the old woman was withholding.

"Is it some sort of a banshee?" Denise's mum asked, and her daughter's mouth dried up with fear.

"Oh thanks for that, mum," Denise said, a little shaken. "I came here for a bit of reassurance, you know."

"No, they've got nothing to do with banshees," said the old woman firmly, then she held out as long as she possibly could to the constant barrage of questioning from Denise and her mother until she finally let it slip. "The Seven Whistlers …" she said in a low voice, and as she did so she exhibited a tremor in her hand.

Denise and her mother looked knowingly at each other; they knew that she always trembled like that when she was afraid of something.

"The Seven Whistlers?" repeated Denise's mum, setting the electric iron in the iron rest of the board. "Who the heck are they? She sat down at the table, anxiously gazing at her mother's sombre face awaiting an answer.

"I'm going back years now," Gran said, looking up at the night sky through the upper panes of the kitchen window, yet in her mind seeing the Liverpool of long ago. "I must have been around twelve when I heard about the Seven Whistlers from my own mother. We were in the backyard of our old house on Walton Lane. I was putting my dad's shirt through the mangle to squeeze out the water, when I heard this peculiar whistling sound. There was something about it that made the hairs on the nape of my neck stand on end. It seemed to come from somewhere up in the sky. Anyway, my mother grabbed me by the arm and pulled me into the house without saying a word. She held me in her arms by the fire and I asked her what was wrong and she told me to be quiet. I struggled free to go and look out of the window, because I could still hear the whistling sound, but she slapped the back of my legs without any explanation and then held me close to her again. It started to rain heavily and yet she stayed where she was, leaving the washing out in the yard to get wet.

"Later that day she told me that bad things were about that could swoop down out of the sky and kill a person. They often killed children, but could also kill grown-ups as well. No one knew what they were. In Wales, my mother's mother believed the Whistlers were the souls of men who had died in a cave-in in the coal mines, but the Whistlers were interpreted as different things in different parts of the country, for they were heard from Land's End to John O'Groats.

"Anyway, that day, when my mother and I heard that whistling sound, something terrible happened; oh, it still upsets me to just think about it, it was so heartbreaking ..." and Gran seemed to be lost in reverie.

"What happened?" prompted Denise's mum.

"It was horrible. A poor boy – he must have been about eight years of age – was playing out in the street near where some workmen were laying boiling tar down in the roadway. For some reason that nobody could quite fathom, their cart tipped over. The tar spilt all over the poor little thing, and the screams ... well, we could hear them in Walton Lane and this happened on Walton Road. His flesh came right off him, it did. Oh, those screams, I'll never forget them. I don't know if it's true but someone said that one of the workmen struck the child's head with a spade to put him out his agony."

"Ooh! What a horrible, sad story," exclaimed Denise, and she cupped her hands tighter around the mug of tea.

Eventually the conversation took a lighter turn, and after a long gossip with the two women, Denise said her goodbyes, kissed the two women and set off for home. At a quarter to twelve, she knocked at her flat but had to let herself in when Martin didn't answer. She found him sitting bolt upright on the sofa, gazing at the window, his eyes wide open and a look of surprise on his face. Somehow, she knew at once that he was dead. She called his name softly and there wasn't an iota of reaction. She touched his shoulder and shook him and his eyes stayed in position but his head dropped forward – lifelessly. Denise frantically tried to shake him out of what she hoped was a trance-like state, until she finally accepted that her boyfriend of five years was dead.

Numb with pain and shock, she mechanically put on her coat and set off for the place she always went when she was in trouble. Almost on auto-pilot, she walked all the way back to her mother's home on Sheil Road, where she finally broke down and cried.

A post mortem was ordered, as it is in any case of sudden death in the young, and Martin's untimely death was ascribed to that loosely-defined term so often used by coroners – natural causes. Apparently, his heart was fine, and Martin seemed to have been in the best of health, and yet he had passed away simply gazing of out the window as he sat on the sofa. In the years since Martin's death Denise has gone over and over the events of that night to try and make sense of it. She came to the conclusion that the strange whistling sound that she, Martin and the gypsy woman had heard that evening must have come from the Seven Whistlers as described by her grandmother and were a warning that something terrible was about to happen.

If the numerous letters and emails that I receive are anything to go by, an uncanny whistling sound has been heard coming from the sky over the north-west for many years, and many who have heard this harmonious sound have claimed that it foretold death. Before I look at a few more of these cases, let me tell you that I have researched this phenomenon extensively, and it seems that the Seven Whistlers have quite a history, stretching back many centuries, but no one seems to be entirely sure as to who, or what, is making the noise. There's a snippet in an old newspaper of 1855 which states:

> *On Friday, 16th March, a collier was asked by a tradesman why he was not at his usual work. The reply was that none of the men had gone to work, because they had heard the "Seven Whistlers" – birds sent by Providence to warn them of an impending danger, and when they heard that signal, not a man would go down the pit.*

The tradesman laughed and accused the collier of being a superstitious fool, but others backed the his strange claim and swore that men had met their deaths down the pits when the spine-chilling shrill music of the Seven Whistlers had been heard in the sky.

Seven fishermen from Folkestone drowned when they dared to go to sea after hearing echoing whistling sounds in the skies over Kent in the 1850s. Their boat was inexplicably overturned on a calm sea and all seven souls perished.

In October 1913, two old Irish sisters by the name of Sweeney caused a commotion in Toxteth when they claimed that the strange haunting pipe music drifting over the rooftops was the work of the legendary bringers of death and disaster – the Seven Whistlers. The sisters were mocked by many in the neighbourhood, including a priest, who dismissed the sounds as being nothing more than the whistling wind from the river, but some of the more superstitious members of the community thought otherwise. The noise from above sounded like so many penny whistles playing some vaguely familiar melody in harmony. On that day – 15 October 1913 – there was a fatal train crash at St James' Station in Toxteth. Six people were killed and twenty-four were injured. The crash had occurred less than a hundred yards from the street where the ethereal penny whistles had been heard shortly before.

One summer evening in the early 1970s, a woman called Phyllis opened the window of her flat in Entwistle Heights, a high-rise tower block that once stood in the Edge Hill district of Liverpool. Phyllis suffered from asthma, and welcomed the fresh evening zephyr that blew gently into her lounge from the open window. She took long, deep breaths and soon felt much better. She stayed by the open window and was looking down at the goings on in the streets below, when she suddenly noticed that her old Jack Russell dog, Kerry, had come to her side and was starting to act very strangely. The little dog whined and tilted her head as she looked up at the window.

"What's the matter with you, Kerry, pet?" Phyllis asked her faithful old canine friend. "Are you missing your walks then?"

The dog suddenly dashed under the table. And more or less simultaneously, Phyllis heard a single high-pitched whistle, followed by several other harmonising notes. The notes blended beautifully and began to play the same melodies over and over again. Then the tempo began to increase rapidly and the notes became more discordant until a cacophony of sound hung in the air. It seemed to come from a spot over Falkner Street, about a hundred feet in the air. Phyllis already knew that the wind could produce some weird and wonderful sounds when it howled against the windows of her high-rise flat, she'd heard them often. But this was definitely different. For a start it was a lovely summer's evening and the weather was perfectly calm and this sound was apparently hanging in the air.

After a while it suddenly lowered in pitch and slowed in rhythm, producing a sound that reminded Phyllis of the noise her nephew made when he swung his novelty toy which was really just a length of plastic tubing. As Phyllis was pondering upon the origins of the sound, there was a sudden violent screech in the street far below. A mini had smashed into a lamppost and a female passenger was thrown straight through the windscreen of the vehicle and on to the pavement where she lay motionless. That girl, aged just nineteen, died from her injuries at the scene of the crash. It later transpired that the car had been stolen by her boyfriend, who survived the crash and fled from the scene without even trying to seek help for his dying girlfriend. As soon as the police and ambulance arrived at the scene, the whistling sound ceased abruptly.

Wind, of course, does create strange sound effects, particularly when it meets tall structures, and eddies and updraughts can produce whistles, shrieks and howls that can sound frightening and unearthly, but the sound that Phyllis heard occurred on a calm evening, and did not seem to be generated by the wind in any way. Is there a rational explanation for the events of that night – or did Phyllis really hear the Seven Whistlers?

HORROR IN ST JAMES'S CEMETRY

Imeet many interesting people in the course of researching my books, and one such person was Richard, who worked as an ambulance man in Liverpool in the 1970s. He told me about a rather curious but grisly incident that took place around 1976.

One evening, at around 11pm, several residents in Gambier Terrace heard a man screaming and the sound seemed to be coming from inside St James's Cemetery, just across the road from the Anglican Cathedral. Two of the residents went to their windows and peered out into the darkness to try and see what was going on. Barely visible by the light of a feeble sodium lamppost, were the three dark outlines of some figures which could be seen moving about inside the cemetery, close to the railings. The screams soon became more urgent and agonising, and so the police were sent for.

A patrol car arrived within minutes and the two police officers were confronted with a very grisly sight on the periphery of the cemetery. They found a man – a well-known vagrant in that area – who had somehow been pushed through the railings with such force, that his ears had almost been scraped off the side of his head and the iron railings had become embedded in his chest and shoulders. An expression of abject terror was etched on the wretch's face, and his eyes were wide open and bulging. They looked as if they were about to burst out of their sockets at any moment.

Richard arrived in an ambulance soon afterwards and examined the man by torchlight in the presence of the policemen. In order to be able to help the poor man, he had to travel some distance along the perimeter until he found a gap in the railings which was wide enough to allow him access to the cemetery. He then inspected the horrific crush wounds on the man's torso and realised that some superhuman force had obviously pressed the man into the railings, as if he were made of Play-Doh. Richard looked about for any evidence that might explain what had happened to the victim, but could find nothing obvious; all was calm and quiet and not a soul stirred in that vast graveyard.

A policeman was radioing the details of the gruesome discovery to Police Headquarters, when he was suddenly interrupted by a chilling incident. The vagrant's body suddenly began to twitch rhythmically. It was as if an electric current was being applied to his body, and his mouth opened and closed spasmodically, like a fish caught in a net. Blood intermingled with saliva dripped from his lips into his beard, and he began to laugh. The laughter was so incongruous in the situation, that Richard recoiled in horror. In the course of his job as an ambulance man he had witnessed all kinds of terrible things. He had occasionally even seen dead bodies trapped in crashed vehicles twitching violently with post-death nerve activity, but he had certainly never seen a dead body laugh, let alone speak, which is what the vagrant did next. The pupils of his eyes had disappeared completely and his bulging white eyeballs were staring up into his forehead, when, in a raspy voice, the man unleashed a string of shocking expletives – then bowed his head and fell silent.

The policemen present knew the tramp well enough to realise that he had spoken in a voice which bore no resemblance to his usual Scottish accent, which, of course, added an additional air of mystery to the whole gruesome episode. It was as if some other person had been talking through the dead man's vocal chords.

Death by misadventure was the coroner's verdict, but something much more sinister was undoubtedly behind the death of that tramp. Just a few years before, a tramp who had been drinking sustained minor injuries after squeezing through a narrow gap in the railings of the same cemetery, after being chased by what he described as a limping, top-hatted ghost. He fled from that cemetery all the way to a priest's residence near the Metropolitan Cathedral. The full story is in the first volume of *Haunted Liverpool*.

In the weeks following the tramp's bizarre death, the residents in the houses facing the scene of the death observed two figures loitering by the cemetery railings, and watched in amazement as they vanished and then reappeared. One witness, who lived on Hope Street, was chatting one night to a few friends about the eerie goings-on at the graveyard and they all determined to uncover the truth behind the mystery. From an agreed date, they all kept vigil on the cemetery railings using binoculars and a telescope. Sure enough, the figures soon made an appearance – and disappearance! One of them was male and the other female, and both were dressed in dark odd-looking clothes. One of the observers shuddered when he caught the woman gazing directly at him – as if she knew he was watching, even from quite a distance away.

As the summer nights lengthened, the figures gradually stopped appearing, until they eventually stopped altogether.

St James's Cemetery is a very special place and has an atmosphere all of its own. Anyone visiting the cemetery cannot help but be aware of this unearthly, secluded atmosphere. Each of the graves seems to have a story to tell – and many of them are truly tragic, often involving children, who died in great numbers, even as late as Edwardian times. The cemetery has been the scene of so many fascinating mysteries, and many of them are documented in my books. Some occultists even go so far as to claim that some portal to a mysterious region exists in that great dormitory of the Victorian and Edwardian dead.

A religious man of my acquaintance once saw something in that cemetery, which left him reeling with shock for days afterwards, but he refused to say just exactly what he had encountered. The only thing he would reveal was this: "I am a Christian and I believe that when you die you sleep until Judgement Day, but some seem to wake before their time."

THE GADSBY ABDUCTION
AND THE GREEN GIRL

Yewtree Cemetery is haunted by the ghost of a woman in black who wears a dark veil covering her face, and she is often seen tripping lightly amongst the gravestones, sometimes even in broad daylight. A few years ago, a group of teenagers who were hanging about in the cemetery came across this ghost as she was wandering rather aimlessly up and down the grassy paths between the graves. At first they just took her to be an ordinary mourner visiting one of the graves, but when they looked more closely they could see that she was dressed in strange old-fashioned clothes, and didn't seem to stop at any one particular plot. Their curiosity aroused, the teenagers started to follow her, keeping some distance behind her, so as not to alert her. She led them out of the cemetery and on to Finch Lane, where she vanished right in front of them.

***

Going further back in time, here is a spooky Edwardian story from that same area of West Derby. This one took place very close to Broughton Hall, in 1908.

That year, at a place called Broughton Terrace, there was an old mansion which stood on Craven Road, owned by a very wealthy man by the name of Peter Walker. One day, one of his servants, a Mrs Gadsby, was putting away some laundry in her mistress's bedroom, when she came upon Mrs Walker's jewellery case. The case was usually kept in a safe, but Mrs Walker had gone out in a hurry that morning and had forgotten to put it away. Knowing that her mistress would be gone for some considerable time, in a rare lapse of her professionalism, Mrs Gadsby decided to take a peek inside the case. She took each of the pieces out of the casket, one at a time, and held them up to the light, enjoying the way in which the jewels sparkled so beautifully in the sun, revealing their true colours.

Mrs Gadsby was usually an honest woman and had earned her position of trust in the Walker household over many years, but on this occasion a little voice inside her began to question why one person should have so much, without even having to work for it, when she and her family had worked hard all their lives and did not possess a single piece of jewellery between them. This thought began to rankle in her and, after checking that none of the other servants was about, she grabbed hold of a diamond brooch and stuffed it down her corset. The brooch was not for herself, but for her daughter, as a wedding gift, as she had recently been married.

It was not long after her return that afternoon that Mrs Walker noticed that the brooch was missing. It was one of her favourite pieces and she always wore it with a particular blouse. All the servants of the house were assembled and questioned about the brooch's disappearance and each of them denied all knowledge. Even though there was no evidence to connect her with the theft, Mrs Gadsby was the prime suspect. As Mrs Walker's lady's maid, she was the only one who was allowed access to her bedroom, and Mrs Walker accused her of stealing it. Though inwardly terrified, the servant pretended to be affronted by the accusation and, unable to come up with any explanation for the disappearance, claimed that the 'Little People' must have taken the brooch. Mrs Gadsby chose this particular explanation to defend herself because she knew that Mrs Walker was a superstitious Dubliner, who had an unshakeable faith in the existence of fairies and pixies and trolls. The servants used to laugh at her behind her back because she was forever talking about the Little People. In an effort to deflect blame from herself, Mrs Gadsby went even further and stated that she had actually seen a tiny man, dressed all in red, running down the cellar steps clutching the brooch. Again she was being quite canny, because, according to Mrs Walker, the fairies always came into the house through a tunnel which led into the cellar.

Mrs Walker told her husband about the theft of the brooch and insisted that he go down into the cellar to investigate. He dutifully obeyed his wife and found a little tunnel in the cellar which was slightly larger than a rat hole, and he immediately had it blocked up.

Three days later, strange rumblings and bangings were heard coming from the cellar, and during the night, the sounds of little footsteps were clearly heard by Mrs Gadsby – and they were making their way up the stairs! She pulled the bedcovers tightly around her and listened again. She suddenly heard a loud peal of thunder outside the window which nearly made her jump out of her skin, followed by sudden heavy rain pattering on the glass. So, in her mind, the servant tried to convince herself that the tiny footsteps might just have been the pattering of the rain on the window panes. Nevertheless, she sat up in bed and lit the bedside candle, feeling distinctly uneasy and apprehensive as to what might happen next.

Just as she was beginning to think that she had been imagining things, her bedroom door suddenly burst open, and in charged a crowd of little men dressed in all sorts of gaily coloured clothes, some of them wearing pointed hats. Mrs Gadsby froze in fear for a moment and then ducked down under the blankets, but the men dived under them and tied little ropes around her ankles and then they all pulled on them – and they managed to drag Mrs Gadsby right out of her bed. She landed on the floor with a loud bump and shouted as loudly as she could for help, but the thunder outside was so deafening that it drowned out her cries. Lightning flashed through the windows and Mrs Gadsby found herself being pulled painfully and inexorably down each of the flights of stairs – towards the cellar. She desperately grabbed at a baluster rail on the way down, but the little men prised her fingers off it and then carried on pulling her down the stairs.

Mrs Gadsby started wailing loudly as she bumped painfully from stair to stair, and her big tomcat, Breslin, who was snoozing in the hallway, curled up in his special hideaway under the stairs, heard her shrieks and woke up in a flash, ready to defend his mistress. He started to attack the little men with tooth and claw, and was finally able to drive them all back down to the cellar, while Mrs Gadsby lay at the bottom of the stairs in a heap in a crumpled heap.

The experience proved to be a salutary one for Mrs Gadsby. She was so terrified of the Little People returning and attacking her once again in the dead of night, that she confessed to the theft of the brooch to Mrs Walker and apologised profusely for her dishonesty and foolishness. Since she had confessed of her own free will, and had always been a loyal and hardworking servant, Mrs Walker forgave her, but not before giving her a long and severe lecture about the perils of dishonesty. She warned her never to steal or tell lies about the Little People again, or they would surely come back to take her again – and this time it might be for good!

On the orders of Mrs Walker, the tunnel in the cellar was unblocked to allow the Little People free access to her house, and Mrs Gadsby kept her cat Breslin on her bed each night from then on … just in case!

Across Liverpool, we move next to Sefton Park, allegedly the home of fairies since the days when the parkland was a vast forest, long before the 2,300-acre Royal Deer Park even existed.

One beautiful spring morning in the year 1893, a twelve-year-old girl named Lucinda sat in the small back garden of Number 111 Ullet Road, the home of her uncle, a Cornish-born blacksmith by the name of Charles Imlach. The girl was staying with her uncle for a month until her father returned from a visit to see his relatives in Ireland. Her mother had died five years previously and there was no one else to take her.

On this spring morning, the air rippled with the fluid notes of Lucinda's fiddle as she played 'Scarborough Fair', and the girl's cousins, Elizabeth and Charles, who were of a similar age to her, were sitting quietly at the end of the garden, drawing pictures. Lucinda's Aunt Margaret was preparing a simple porridge breakfast for the children at the hob in the kitchen, and when the meal was ready, she went outside to call them when she saw that Lucinda, Charles and Elizabeth were standing in a corner of the garden, avidly gazing at something amongst the bushes. She called to the children, but they didn't respond, so she called again. Eventually the boy and the two girls broke out of their spell and came running into the kitchen, each claiming to have seen a 'green girl' who, they said, had been sitting on the garden wall amongst the tangles of ivy. Margaret Imlach smiled and shook her head. She naturally assumed that childish imagination was behind the strange claims, and took no further notice of their tall story.

"Mmm, I'm sure," she said under her breath, and then more loudly, "Now come and wash your hands, my dears, and we'll decide what to do with the rest of the day."

That afternoon, Margaret took the children to nearby Sefton Park, where they gambolled about in the spring sunshine as she pushed the perambulator containing her one-year-old child Mary. As she and Mary fed the ducks on the boating lake, the three children ran off into a wooded area and went missing for a while. Margaret called for them repeatedly, and when the unruly trio finally returned, they once again claimed that they had seen the tiny green girl and told Margaret that she was clothed in a dress made entirely of leaves and that her name was Eleetra.

Mrs Imlach smiled and again believed that the children were merely acting out some childish fantasy – until she saw Eleetra herself, perched on the branch of a nearby tree, almost perfectly camouflaged because of the green hue of her skin and her clothes made of interwoven leaves. Even the child's hair was of a ferny green colour. Margaret audibly gasped in shock, scarcely able to believe the evidence of her own eyes. Her reaction seemed to alarm the green girl, who instantly scrambled off along a branch, and was soon out of sight amongst the profusion of sycamore leaves. Margaret Imlach told the children that they were to leave the park at once. She felt certain that the green child was something unnatural and sinister, and she hurried away from the woods pushing the perambulator, and dragging Charles by his hand, because he and Lucinda and Elizabeth were so reluctant to leave their new found friend.

It would seem that Eleetra made many more visits to that house on Ullet Road, and that Lucinda was so anxious to keep in touch with the mysterious 'nature spirit' – which is what she believed Eleetra to be – that she arranged to stay every weekend at her aunt's home, even after her father had returned from Ireland. Unfortunately, when she reached the age of fourteen, Lucinda was forced to move away from England, her cousins and Eleetra, because her father had decided to start a new life in Australia.

However, the Imlach children and many other people continued to see the green girl for many years after her departure, right up until the end of the Edwardian era, in fact.

Was Eleetra merely a figment of a child's mind's eye? or was she a real entity, possibly indeed some kind of nature spirit?

A Prisoner's Free Spirit

O ver the years I have read of many intriguing tales, sent to me by letter, from prisoners in Walton Gaol who have had strange paranormal experiences whilst being incarcerated behind bars, and this story is just one of these.

Late one night, back in the early 1970s, Michael, an Anfield man, drove a transit van to a building site up in Huyton. Earlier that day he had spotted a heap of copper pipes on the site, as well as a few other items which he knew he could sell for scrap. He pulled up his van, turned off the lights and parked it in a secluded spot next to the building site fence. He sat quietly in the van for a while, checking that no one was about. Then, using wire-cutters, he neatly removed a large rectangular section of the fence and then niftily backed the transit van through the gap he had created and on to the building site. He was a past master at this type of operation, and making virtually no noise, he opened the vehicle's back door, and started loading all the copper pipes into the vehicle. There were lots of them, far more than he'd expected, and in his mind he was calculating how much the loot was worth and what he would do with the cash.

About five minutes later, a police patrol car pulled up near this Huyton building site and soon discovered the gaping hole in the fence. A policeman shone a torch straight at Michael's face.

"What's going on here?" he asked, correctly assuming that he had caught Michael in the act of stealing the pipes.

Most people at that point would have frozen in fear, made a run for it, or stammered out some silly excuse, but Michael casually said, "Late delivery. Just delivering some pipes, mate."

The policeman walked over to Michael, who was only too happy to elaborate further.

"I've been rushed off me feet today making deliveries. The wife'll be wondering where I am."

And he started to remove the copper pipes from the van, and put them back where he'd found them. By pure luck – because he must have seen the gaping hole in the fence – the policeman swallowed the story and went back to his vehicle and drove off. When he was sure that the coast was clear, Michael then cheekily loaded all the copper pipes back into the transit van and sped off home. The next morning he got up early and drove to a certain scrap dealer in Liverpool and received quite a few bob for the pipes.

It just so happened that later that day, Michael went to visit his brother-in-law Tony in Walton Gaol, and during the visit, Tony whispered to him, "Hey, mate! Did you take some stuff from a site in Huyton last night?"

Michael shifted in his seat. He couldn't say too much in case the warders overheard him, but he wondered how on earth his brother-in-law had found out about the theft of the copper pipes – he'd only just got rid of them! He concluded that someone at the scrap yard must have said something to someone, who had in turn had passed the information to someone else during another prison visit. If that was the case, news certainly had travelled fast, because this was the day after the theft.

A few months later, after his release, Tony told Michael the full story of how he came to know about the building site theft, and it seemed ludicrously far-fetched, but Tony swore that it was true. A prisoner named Rob – a civil servant serving two years for fraud – shared a cell with Tony, and this cellmate, who was into Eastern mysticism and Yoga, taught Tony how to meditate. Rob also told Tony that he could travel out of his body under certain conditions, and he called this routine 'astral travelling'.

Tony was naturally doubtful about his cellmate's claims, but that night, after the lights went out, Rob gave a demonstration of his so-called astral-travelling. He sat cross-legged on his bunk, and remained silent and motionless for what seemed like an hour to Tony, but was, in fact, a duration of about twenty minutes. During that time, Rob's mind journeyed to a place that Tony had asked him to visit – The Wooky Hollow club on Belmont Road. Rob visited the place and said that he'd seen P J Proby singing at the club. Tony had shown a photograph of his wife to rob and had asked him to see if he could see her at the club, as she went there most nights, but Rob said that he hadn't been able to see her during his clairvoyant visit. Tony wasn't convinced that Rob was telling the truth, so he asked him to visit the house of his brother-in-law, Michael. He gave Rob Michael's address, and Tony assumed the cross-legged posture once again and this time, he remained totally silent and still for about forty minutes.

When he came to, he told Tony that he had tracked Michael as he drove from his home in the transit van, and had seen him trying to steal the copper pipes from the building site and the policeman shining the torch at him. Rob had later visited Michael and seen that he was having an affair with Tony's wife, Rita. He was surprised by Tony's reaction when he delivered this body blow, because his cellmate just smiled and shook his head. He said that he was actually amused by this new revelation, as he no longer cared for her romantically, and the girl had given up on her jailbird husband because he was always in and out of prison.

Around 1980, it was alleged that Rob had died in a fire at his home in Spain during one of his astral jaunts. There is no evidence to support these claims, but it was said that Rob had been travelling about in his astral body while his home caught fire and his physical body was burnt. Would his astral body therefore be doomed to roam the 'astral planes' for evermore?

THE DOWNRIGHT STRANGE

Whilst writing and researching the *Haunted Liverpool* series, I have received quite a staggering volume of emails and letters from readers, and whenever I have been invited as a guest on local radio programmes, I have generated a record number of telephone calls – such is the intense interest in the paranormal in the Merseyside area. A sizeable percentage of the emails, letters and telephone calls relate to what I can only describe as stories of the downright strange. Here are just a few examples of these exceedingly odd, and often frightening supernatural incidents.

As I write these words I have, hanging on my wall before me, a framed photograph of Bold Street, taken around 1890. The photographer is unknown, but when he took his snapshot he must have been standing close to Number 66 Bold Street, the address of a popular photographer's studio, in the late nineteenth century, and whose proprietor's name was Jones. Now, in the twenty-first century, it is the premises of the Meet Brazilian Bar and Restaurant. This photograph is said to be haunted by an alarming apparition, which has terrified a number of children over the years.

There are many reported cases of images paranormally coming to 'life' in photographs and paintings. For example, at the village of Limpias in Spain, in 1919, hundreds of people – many of them 'scientifically educated persons' – signed affidavits stating that they had seen 'certain pictures of saints performing miracles, stepping out of their panels, and carrying out actions'. Flaws in the retina of the human eye, religious mania and hysteria were cited as explanations for these weird, but well-witnessed incidents.

When a picture of Christ in a church at Mirebeau in France started bleeding in 1911, the rationalists attempted to explain the phenomenon by stating that the 'blood' from the picture was actually just paint, but extensive tests on the liquid, carried out at the Lister Institute in London, proved conclusively that it was human blood, and of an exceptionally rare type.

So much for paintings that bleed, or exhibit supernatural animation, but what about photographs? Well, I personally know of many photographs that are allegedly haunted. For example, there is the photograph of one John G Sutton, the gamekeeper of Old Langho in Lancashire, taken in 1908. The photograph is a fairly ordinary one, simply showing Mr Sutton standing outside his cottage, and yet various people over the years have claimed that Mr Sutton's image moves from time to time in the photograph.

And so back to the photograph of Bold Street that hangs before me on my wall in its frame. It depicts St Luke's Church in the distance at the top of the street, and the photographer must have positioned himself in the right half of the roadway when he captured the scene, which features a horse-drawn omnibus trundling up the street towards St Luke's Church, and an assortment of pedestrians either walking along, or window-shopping. This street scene then, is interesting though unremarkable, and is typical of many photographs of the late-Victorian period, with its subjects frozen forever like statues. Their images remain, whilst the flesh and blood counterparts of these monochrome people have long departed for their graves. But sometimes, it would seem, the camera captures something else that cannot be explained by the laws of optics as we formulate them today.

One night, in 1977, the photograph hanging on my wall hung in the spare bedroom of a house on Breeze Hill, Walton. Seven-year-old Patricia and her five-year-old brother Peter, were staying with their Auntie Florence and Uncle George for the weekend. At 8.30pm, the children were taken to the spare room by Aunt Flo, as they called her, and tucked up in the old double bed. Aunt Flo promised her nephew and niece that she would take them to a toyshop on the following morning, if they were good children and went straight to sleep. She kissed them both goodnight and then went downstairs.

About ten minutes after the light in the spare bedroom had been turned out, Peter fell asleep, but Patricia didn't feel at all tired, she was excited about the prospect of going to the toy shop in the morning, and her eyes wandered across the walls of the room, subconsciously studying all the details of the wallpaper and furniture. By the light of the lamppost shining into the room, the girl's eyes eventually lighted on the old black and white photograph of Bold Street hanging on the wall. Her eyes widened as something suddenly started move in that photograph. Patricia thought that it was a spider crawling about in the middle of the picture at first – but then she heard the faint sounds of someone running. She assumed that they were the footfalls of someone outside in the street, until she noticed that the sound was unmistakably coming from inside the room, and so she sat up in the bed and tried to determine exactly where in the room they were coming from. Then she spotted the running figure in black – in the photograph on the wall! Laughter also rang out from the Bold Street picture, and she had to accept that the sound of the running feet was definitely coming from the photograph.

The girl was naturally alarmed, and she watched in suspense as a man with a sinister, menacing face, came running towards her down the street in the picture; initially only visible as a small black speck, but then getting larger by the second, until he eventually filled the entire photograph. He wore a bowler hat, and beneath the brim of the hat, a pair of dark-rimmed eyes gazed at Patricia with an evil, penetrating stare.

She did not care to wait and see what the man would do next, but instead, she flung back the bedcovers and ran screaming from the room. She thundered down the stairs in a dreadful state to her aunt and uncle. With her heart pounding, she started to give an incoherent account of what had taken place, and when her Uncle George heard the sobbing child say that there was a man upstairs, he thought the worst and grabbed a poker from the fireside and bounded up the stairs to the spare bedroom, expecting to confront an intruder. He found no man there – just little Peter, who was now sitting up in the bed, rubbing his sleepy eyes, unaware of the drama that was unfolding around him.

Aunt Flo tried to convince Patricia that she had experienced nothing more sinister than a nightmare, but she flatly refused to sleep in that room, no matter how hard they tried to persuade her and so, the nephew and niece ended up sleeping with their aunt in her bed, while Uncle George spent the night in the spare bedroom. He experienced nothing untoward that night and slept soundly.

Months later, Patricia and her brother were staying at the house again, and once more they slept in the spare bedroom, despite Patricia's reservations. Once again, the weird man in black was seen in the Bold Street photograph, this time peeping from the doorway of a shop. On this occasion, Peter saw the man too, and he and Patricia hugged one another in trepidation as they watched him, but their fear gradually subsided and they became fascinated by the antics of the bowler-hatted man as he flitted out from the doorway and hid behind the horse-drawn omnibus. He kept peeping out at them, before running into the shadowy side of Bold Street where he vanished. Moments later the man reappeared much closer, so that the features of his face could be clearly seen, and he scowled at the children. His face became contorted and twisted and he waved his fist threateningly at them.

Young Peter started to cry, saying, "I don't like that nasty man. Make him go away, Pat."

Patricia yelled at the top of her voice for Uncle George. As soon as she heard his reassuring footsteps coming up the stairs, the man in the photograph turned and ran off into the distance, where he hid in another doorway. Uncle George came into the room and switched on the light. Patricia told him about the same 'ghost' haunting the photograph. He didn't know what to make of it; he could see that both his nephew and niece were obviously upset by the picture, but it didn't make any sense. He looked closely at the picture and said, half to himself, "How the Dickens could a ghost be in a photograph?"

"He's there, Uncle. Look! Look!" shouted Patricia, frantically pointing to something in the photograph.

Uncle George could see only the eternally motionless and anonymous people in the photograph, but he squinted closely at them all the same.

"He's standing at the top of the street, keeping still, so you won't notice him," Patricia told her uncle, and she knelt at the end of the bed and pointed the figure out to him.

"Show me," said her uncle and lifted the child right up to the photograph and felt her recoil and tremble in his hands.

She squirmed to be let down and said that the figure had just run off and vanished. Uncle George glanced back at the picture and noticed that the figure he had seen moments before standing at the top of the street in the photograph, had now disappeared.

He scratched his head in disbelief.

"Well I never!" he exclaimed. "What the heck's going on?"

A year later, Patricia's uncle died from smoke inhalation after an electric blanket at his home caught fire. Aunt Flo managed to escape unharmed but she never got over her husband's untimely death. She moved to Tuebrook for a while, and then went to live in Halewood, but she never again felt settled. Patricia and Peter's parents moved to Surrey and so they lost touch with their favourite aunt, and Flo sadly passed away in the late 1980s.

In 1996, Patricia married a Liverpool man and moved back to her hometown. At the wedding party she met many of her cousins whom she hadn't seen for ages, and one of them, a young man named Daniel, told her a story that sent a shudder down her spine. He told her that he had once slept at his Auntie Flo's house when she was living on Marlborough Road in Tuebrook. In the room in which Daniel slept there was an old framed photograph of a street; he couldn't remember which street it was, but what he had seen in that photograph had been imprinted in his mind for many years. Daniel told a spellbound Patricia about a man in a bowler hat who had moved about in that photograph and taunted him until he had become so paralysed with terror that he had been unable to cry out for his aunt. Patricia immediately recalled the two similar incidents from her own childhood when she had seen the very same thing in the photograph, and she and Daniel compared notes. It was soon apparent that childhood imagination was not to blame, because how could three separate people – Peter, Patricia and Daniel – independently dream up the same bizarre and frightening character? The mystery deepened when another cousin, Laura, said that she also remembered seeing a dark shape moving about in the same photograph on the wall of Aunt Flo's spare bedroom. The only difference was that Laura did not see the man in the bowler hat, merely an indistinct, amorphous shadow-like thing that darted about in the photograph.

It is difficult to explain the phenomenon of the man who apparently haunted the photograph, and such incidents make me wonder if there are beings in higher dimensions than ourselves who can somehow access two-dimensional photographs, as if they were three dimensional. Here's another example of the downright strange, and it's a mystery that has resisted a rational solution for quite a few years now.

***

Around 1989 a man in his early twenties by the name of Tom was looking for his friend Billy, who had an apartment on Rodney Street. Tom had had an argument with his family and had stormed out of his home in Toxteth at around 9.45pm. He walked the streets until about 10.20pm, and then decided to call on his friend Billy, a man in his late twenties who had lived close to Tom for a few years. If Billy was at home, Tom intended to ask him if he could stay the night rather than go back home, as he was too proud to make up with his mother and father, with whom he'd had a blazing row.

Tom wasn't sure if Billy lived at Number 10 Rodney Street or Number 20, but he called at Number 10 at around 10.25pm. There were a few intercom buttons at the side of the door and Tom pressed the bottom one randomly. A few moments later, someone unlocked the door from the inside and left it slightly

80

ajar, so Tom pushed the door slightly and called out, "Billy, it's me ... Tom."

No one answered, so Tom pushed the door further open, and suddenly the dark interior was lit up to reveal a sight that left Tom dumbfounded.

The hallway looked gigantic – much too big even for one of the grand Georgian town houses on Rodney Street, and there was an unearthly light radiating from a range of towering bookshelves, which stretched up to an impossibly high ceiling. What was even more surreal, was the presence of a hooded monk in a cowl who stood in the middle of the hallway.

"Are you Tom?" he asked, in a deep, resonating voice from beneath the cowl.

"Er ... yes," stammered Tom.

The monk beckoned to him with some urgency and glided off down an aisle that ran between the stacks of enormous bookshelves, which were crammed with dusty leather-bound volumes. The monk started to speak in what sounded like English inter-mingled with Latin phrases, and Tom walked alongside him as they strolled on for what seemed like the best part of a mile. The place was reminiscent of the inside of Dr Who's Tardis; it seemed to have an impossibly large interior, which bore no relation to the actual size of the house. At the end of another long and unintelligible line of dialogue, the monk stopped abruptly, and studied Tom's face in a suspicious manner – as if he had suddenly realised that he had mistaken the young man for someone else. The monk then turned sharply around, and taking hold of Tom's elbow, marched him back along the looming corridors in silence. When they finally reached the front door he muttered something that may have been, "Sorry". Without another word by way of explanation, he opened the door and gently pushed Tom back on to the doorstep, where he stood in bewilderment as the door was shut in his face.

Tom never managed to find Billy's flat that night – not surprising, as it turned out that he had moved to another flat on Bedford Street South. So he found himself with no choice but to swallow his pride and return home. The argument was soon forgotten, and he decided to tell his parents and sister about the impossible house at Number 10 Rodney Street. They reasoned that he'd probably just mistakenly found himself in the house of a religious monastic order; and the houses on Rodney Street were quite large inside anyway. Tom tried to explain to them that the house he had visited had been cavernous inside; out of all proportion to any of the houses on Rodney Street.

He called at Number 10 to satisfy his curiosity on the next day, and found that the hallway was tiny in comparison with the huge hall he had seen the night before. To this day, Tom doesn't not understand what he stumbled into that night in the late 1980s.

I have learned many strange things in the course of my investigations of the paranormal over the years, and one conclusion I've definitely come to is that time and space are not as straightforward as we like to imagine. Many readers have experienced what are known as 'timeslips' – strange episodes where a person may find that he or she has walked into the past or future, but, it would seem there are also 'spaceslips'. These are less common than timeslips, but just as intriguing and inexplicable, and there have been quite a number of them reported to me over the years. I have even compiled a map of these 'hyperspace fields' (as I call them), which seem to shrink distances in a way that modern physics cannot explain.

***

A few years ago a mother and her daughter were cycling through Halewood Country Park, when they suddenly found themselves on Woolton's Camp Hill – a mile and a quarter away. The mother was naturally flummoxed, and she and her daughter turned around and started to cycle back in the direction of the park – only to find themselves back in the Halewood park within a few minutes, rather than the quarter of an hour or so it should have taken. The mother met a neighbour named Norman at the Halewood park who was also out cycling, and after she told him about the incredible cycling trip, he revealed that the exact same thing had happened to him three years previously. All three then set out on their bikes, hoping to experience the bizarre short-cut once again, but this time the distance was not compressed.

Science fiction writers have used the concept of hyperspace as a useful method for getting round the faster-than-light problem posed by Einstein. Space as we know it seems empty and straightforward enough, but in reality it is anything but empty; it is swarming with all sorts of subatomic particles and has numerous dimensions, and many physicists believe it is possible to slip into secret 'back alleyways' of space to get to a destination in the past or future, far removed from the starting point. In theory, we would have to find a way to move at right angles to every possible direction in our space in order to access a higher dimension, but there may be simpler ways of travelling through hyperspace.

A single cubic centimetre of space would, to our eyes, seem smooth and empty, but in reality it isn't. Let us simplify it a bit and imagine the cube of space has had the atmosphere sucked out of it. It still isn't empty. On the quantum scale, that cube is 'foaming' with fluctuations of energy, so that in the space that fills a cubic centimetre, there is energy equivalent to the mass of about ten to the power of 91 kilogrammes. The conversion of just one kilogramme releases more energy than a 20-megaton nuclear warhead. Now, scientists have realised that the foaming structure of space invites the strong possibility of openings from one region of space to another. The two openings could be parsecs, light years, miles, or hundreds of feet apart, and these openings are known in the scientific community as wormholes. They may be only centimetres long, yet they run outside of space and meander back again at a distant point. The rules of Relativity actually allow these short-cuts in space, and who knows, perhaps these openings in the very fabric of space will provide humankind with a way of getting to the stars. They may also throw some light on the spaceslips I have mentioned in this section.

***

The final story in this chapter fits in quite well with the theme of the downright strange. At a certain office in Liverpool in the 1990s, a coffee-making machine was installed, and not long afterwards, a variety of paranormal incidents started to take place, and most of them were witnessed by a woman called Brenda, a secretary in the firm.

The first incident started in the summer of 1997. Brenda was seated at her word-processor one morning at 9.45am, creating application forms for her boss, when she saw something very peculiar indeed. Something dark flitted into the office via the gap under the door, and it moved towards the new coffee machine, where it vanished. As Brenda stared fixedly at the carpet by the machine, wondering if she had merely seen some shadow of a bird flying past outside the window, her workmate Lyndsay sauntered into the office, late as usual. She started to give an elaborate explanation as to why she was late but realised that Brenda was not listening to her. She seemed to be distracted by something. Her two other workmates, Dean and Brian, who usually shared the office with them, were both off work for a few days having succumbed to a vicious flu bug that was doing the rounds of the building.

Lyndsay went to the coffee machine and pressed a few buttons whilst continuing to talk to Brenda, when suddenly, the neon lights in the ceiling began to flicker on and off. The word-processor's screen froze, and Brenda swore under her breath. She moved the computer mouse frantically to try and get the computer to respond, but the arrow pointer stayed firmly put on the monitor screen. She was forced to restart the computer, losing all the hard work she had been doing since arriving in the process.

At 10.10am the boss, Tony, came into the office and told Lyndsay off because she had sent the wrong batch of forms to a client, and as he berated her, Brenda again saw the shadow she had seen earlier, and this time her blood froze. The shadow looked as if it was a cut-out of a man's head and shoulders, and it slid out from under the coffee machine.

"Oh my God!" gasped Brenda, and as she did so, the silhouette withdrew, and slid back under the coffee dispenser.

Tony and Lyndsay were still arguing about the forms, totally unaware of the bizarre apparition. Brenda kept staring at the base of the dispenser, but the thing never reappeared. At about 11.30am, Lyndsay went to the toilet, and Brenda walked over to the coffee machine and crouched down slightly. She looked at the carpet at the base of the machine and wondered if some of the liquid had perhaps leaked out, but there was no stain there and the carpet was completely dry. The secretary began to worry if she was seeing things; perhaps she had spent too much time staring at a computer screen. She knew that she didn't take enough breaks, and got lots of headaches as a result.

When it came to one o'clock, and her lunchbreak, Brenda walked to a nearby park; keen to get out of the office which she had found more and more oppressive as the morning wore on. It was a fine sunny afternoon, perfumed with summer's flowers. Brenda sat down on a bench in a sunny position and opened a sandwich pack. She gazed idly at the office block where she had worked now for seven years, and she suddenly noticed a stranger at her window. She could see that it wasn't Tony, or anyone else she recognised from that building. He was quite tall, and wore what looked like a camel hair coat. The man was visible for about ten minutes and then left the window. Brenda kept her eyes fixed on the entrance doors of the building and expected to see the stranger coming out at any minute, but he never did, and so, perplexed, she cut short her lunch break and returned to the office.

She told Tony and Lyndsay about the man she'd seen in the office and asked who he was, but they had not seen anyone either entering or leaving the building. Tony had remained in his office across the corridor from Brenda's and he was certain that no one had passed his door. Lyndsay had been smoking a cigarette as she chatted to a security guard in the parking area at the back of the building, and no one had passed them. Brenda suddenly felt really silly, she shouldn't have told them about what she had seen. Tony suggested that perhaps she'd been working a little too hard.

"As soon as Dean and Brian are back, you can take a few days off. You look as though you need it," he told her.

On the following morning, Brenda was working on a spreadsheet on her computer, and Lyndsay was checking some invoices when the entire room suddenly shuddered, as if the building had been hit by an earth tremor. Lyndsay let out a yelp, and Tony came into the office a few moments later and asked, "What was that? Did you feel it?"

"Yes, but I've no idea what it was, but I know didn't like it," said Brenda.

When they made enquiries they found that the jolt had not been not felt on the floors below, and so Tony lamely surmised that it had been some kind of vibration, perhaps caused by some passing heavy-goods vehicle.

That afternoon, Lyndsay suddenly stopped typing and looked over at Brenda with a serious expression on her face. With a shudder, the young secretary told Brenda that something had just stroked her hair. It had felt like a cold hand on the crown of her head, stroking in a circular motion for a few moments.

Brenda was already convinced that something strange was going on at the office, but was at a loss to explain just what was unfolding. About twenty minutes later, both secretaries heard a man's faint voice calling Lyndsay's name on her desk intercom. The whispering voice uttered several other words that couldn't be understood. Lyndsay announced that she'd had enough. Without further ado, the terrified secretary picked up her bag and belongings and left the office. Tony was furious when he saw her storming down the corridor and came into Brenda's room to ask what was going on. Brenda told him that Lyndsay had heard voices on the intercom and had felt a hand touching her head; she had been so spooked that she had left the building.

"Humph! Any excuse and that one downs tools!" snapped Tony. "I've never heard such a load of nonsense in my life."

With that he marched back into his office in a rage and slammed the door behind him.

Brenda was now left alone in the office and she felt so afraid. She was absolutely convinced that there was something in that office with her – watching her every move – and when its presence grew strong, she felt goosebumps rising on her arms. The warm sunlight streaming into the office was now somehow being blocked out by the subtle manifestation, and Brenda felt more and more uneasy by the minute. She found it almost impossible to concentrate on her work in this situation, and she decided that she also had to leave the office, however unprofessional it may seem to Tony. Brenda rose from her seat, getting ready to go, when suddenly the door opened, and in walked a tall, debonair-looking man in his fifties. He wore a long knee-length camel-hair coat, and Brenda instantly recognised him as the man she'd seen in the office the day before as she sat in the park.

"Ah, Brenda, have you seen anything strange in here recently?" asked the man in a calm voice.

"Who are you?" Brenda asked, naturally suspicious of the stranger. "What are you doing here?"

The man said that he was a civil servant, but gave no more details. He then proceeded towards the coffee machine. He produced a small toolkit from his inside pocket and proceeded to use the screwdrivers and other instruments to remove a panel on the coffee machine. As Brenda looked on, intrigued, she asked him what he was doing, and the man explained that the coffee dispenser was in the wrong place, and that it was causing the strange incidents that Brenda had been experiencing. The man talked about feng-shui, and said that sometimes electrical machinery could upset delicate currents which, in turn, could disturb the harmony of things that most people didn't even know about.

Brenda didn't have a clue what the man was going on about, and she decided that he must be unbalanced, so she sneaked out of the office, whilst his back was turned, and tiptoed across the corridor to tell Tony about him. But Tony was in the middle of an important business call and kept gesturing for Brenda to be quiet, while she gestured even more frantically in an effort to get him to listen to her. Some ten minutes elapsed, before Tony finally put the receiver down and in a patronising voice asked Brenda what was the matter. She told him about the stranger in her office and how he was dismantling the coffee machine. Tony looked at her quizically, then left his desk and crossed the corridor to Brenda's office, shaking his head.

There was no one in the office, but the coffee machine had been moved about six or seven inches to the right of its original position. Tony began to seriously worry about Brenda's mental health, and wondered if she was having some kind of nervous breakdown, but she was adamant that a man claiming to be a civil servant had entered the office minutes earlier. Tony was still dubious, but he had to admit that the coffee machine had moved and he knew that it was far too heavy and bulky for Brenda to have moved it. It was a complete mystery.

That man was never seen or heard from again, and, to the relief of Lyndsay and Brenda, there were no more incidents of paranormal activity in the office after that day.

Brenda still believes that there was something supernatural about the man who came into her office and I agree with her. I think that he may have been someone sent by a higher authority, to perhaps 'fix' some portal that was opened by – of all things – the electrical system of a mundane coffee dispenser. In the same month as I received the account of this story, a man who worked in India Buildings told me a similar story about a smartly-dressed man in a pin-striped suit who used to be spotted in several parts of the building. The man was always taken to be a member of the living, since he appeared as solid as the next person, until he would turn a corner in a corridor and vanish without a trace. Only then did people realise that he was actually a ghost. That man was also described as suave and well-groomed in appearance – remember that Brenda described the stranger in her office as 'debonair'. Perhaps apparitions of this type are not ghosts at all but agents of some higher force, attending to metaphysical matters that we can't even begin to comprehend.

THE GHOST OF ELIZABETH PEERS

S ome ghosts are undoubtedly the visible impressions left by a particularly terrible or traumatic event. The following haunting is a typical case in point. In the 1980s, a ghostly girl enveloped in a cloak was seen on numerous occasions walking down Lodge Lane and several of the nearby streets between Edge Hill and Toxteth. I once knew someone who had actually seen the phantom girl, and he was not a man who was given to telling lies or fanciful tales. In fact, he had absolutely no interest in ghosts or anything to do with the paranormal and had rather a shallow, pragmatic philosophy of life which left no room for the supernatural.

It was a surprise to his wife, therefore, when she heard him frantically yelling her name as he hammered on the front door of their home one evening in 1982. The man, John, lived with his wife at a house on Scholar Street at the time, and he had been returning from the nearby Boundary pub on the corner of Lodge Lane and Smithdown Road when he came upon the apparition. It was a little after 11pm, and there was a light drizzle that night. Just one person – an old man – passed him, and John afterwards remembered that he had mused that Smithdown Road was unusually quiet that night, even for midweek.

All of a sudden he came across the eerie-looking figure of a girl. She was aged about twelve, in his estimation, and wore a beret and a long cloak. Her face was a deathly white, as were her frail little hands. Her eyes were huge and black and as lifeless as a doll's.

She walked slowly towards him, an awful low moaning sound coming from her open mouth. John felt the hairs on the back of his neck begin to prickle, and goose-pimples simultaneously rose up on his arms and legs. He just knew instinctively that the sinister-looking figure was not a living child, but some phantasm of the dead. John didn't hang around to find out and ran all the way to his home, too afraid to look back. He clung tightly to his wife in bed all that night, and the couple heard the distinct sounds of a child crying outside for an hour after he arrived home.

The ghost which John had encountered was seen a few days later, this time by a man on his way to work at around 6.30 in the morning. The description was more or less exactly the same, but the second witness described the beret that John had seen as a tam o'shanter. Like John, this second witness was spooked by the pallid-faced apparition, and he hurried down Longfellow Street in a state of fright, glancing back over his shoulder several times to check whether the ghost was following him. Thankfully, it wasn't. It just stood on the corner, motionless, staring after him.

Similar reports to these continued for a while, after which the ghost made itself increasingly scarce. It is still occasionally seen, but nowhere near as frequently as it was in the 1980s. I decided to research the case, and in doing so, unearthed a tragic tale.

Back in the year 1905, the Peers family lived at Number 64 Wendell Street, off Smithdown Road. The family had originally lived on Bective Street, off Earle Road, but had moved to Wendell Street around 1902. The head of the family was forty-seven-year-old William Peers, a bricklayer by trade. He and his forty-three-year-old wife Elizabeth had five sons and a beautiful, intelligent daughter also named Elizabeth.

Around midnight on Saturday, 28 October 1905, Mrs Peers sent her daughter to a butcher's shop on Lodge Lane to buy some cooked pork. The child was given sixpence and a plate on which to carry the pork home, and so she set off on her errand. In that day and age, the junction of Smithdown Road and Lodge Lane formed part of a thickly populated neighbourhood, where the shops stayed open later than usual on Saturday nights, and the electric tramcars continued to run after midnight. Elizabeth wore a smart dress, a long cloak, and a tam o'shanter on her head, and presented quite a pretty sight trotting down the busy street. She set off from her home in Wendell Street and headed down Longfellow Street towards Lodge Lane.

Elizabeth Peers never returned from that errand.

Mrs Peers had a married brother who lived nearby, and sometimes Elizabeth called in to see him when the mood took her, and so when the child didn't return from the butcher's by 1am, Mrs Peers assumed that she was at her uncle's home. However, the hours wore on, and soon Mrs Peers and her husband John began to seriously worry for their child's safety. They hoped and prayed that nothing had happened to her. They had already ascertained through some other relatives that Elizabeth was not staying with her uncle. What then, had become of her?

On the following morning, which was a Sunday, at 8.35am, a little eight-year-old girl named Frances Myles, who had been sent to fetch a jug of milk from a shop, skipped through the entry that backed on to Cullen Street – just three streets along from Wendell Street – when she came upon a girl lying on her back. The little girl didn't fully take in the significance of the ghastly scene, but simply ran home and babbled about a girl who had fainted in the entry. The girl's mother took no notice.

Meanwhile, a young carter named William Wilson, came out of his backyard, on his way to work at a local stable, when he noticed something lying on the cobbled ground of the gloomy entry. At first he thought it was an old bundle of tarpaulin, but when he stooped and examined the 'object', he found that it was a beautiful girl lying on her back. She was lying on some sort of cloak, which had been uncoupled from around her neck and placed under her body, doubling as a blanket. A tam o'shanter which the girl had obviously been wearing was lying nearby. The girl had one arm raised up in a peculiar and grotesque way, for that arm had been deformed and twisted out of shape as if something heavy had crushed it.

The girl seemed to be about nine or ten years of age, and her eyes were wide open, as was her mouth, but she was obviously dead. The expression that was etched on her face was one of extreme shock. Her skin was as pale as snow and there were strange small black bruises all over her face, and the carter also noticed bruising on her throat, as if the girl had been strangled. The flesh on one side of her face was puffy and swollen, as if someone had hit her really hard. The body had been thoroughly drenched by the downpour that had lasted from about three o'clock in the morning.

The carter quickly raised the alarm, and the body was taken to a nearby house, where resuscitation was attempted but soon found to be a waste of time. The child was dead. The body was taken to the Southern Hospital, where doctors officially pronounced life extinct. The Peers family feared the worst when they heard about the girl's body being found in the entry, and they later identified their child as being their ten-year-old daughter, Elizabeth Peers.

On 31 October, a post mortem examination revealed that the child had been raped as well as murdered. She had died from suffocation and shock to her genitals, caused by being simultaneously choked and raped by a person or persons unknown.

On Friday, 3 November at 3pm, Elizabeth Peers was buried at Toxteth Park Cemetery on Smithdown Road. An incredible thirty thousand people attended the funeral, which was conducted by the vicar of St Clement's Church. After the burial service, the vicar raged against the atrocity, saying that an outrage had undoubtedly been committed on the poor child, in open defiance of the Commandments. In his denouncement, the vicar said that Heaven was angry with the wicked man who had perpetrated the foul deed, and that God had sharpened his sword against him. One of the many touching floral tributes adorning the coffin and graveside was a wreath from Tiber Street School, the school that Elizabeth Peers had attended. A smaller wreath from a playmate at this school, simply read 'Lizzie'.

The murderer of Elizabeth Peers was glimpsed by several witnesses that night, and to me the descriptions strike a rather familiar note. Mr G A Wolstenholme, was returning to his home that night after a trip to Widnes, and when he reached the corner of Cullen Street, between 1.15am and 1.20am, he noticed a man coming out of the back entry of Cullen Street. The man looked alarmed and agitated. He described him as being between around thirty-four to forty years of age, about 5 feet 10 inches in height and wearing a dark moustache. Another witness also spotted this same man at around 11.15pm, close to the murder scene.

The police subsequently discovered that the killer had taken Elizabeth Peers into an empty house on Cullen Street and raped and murdered her there, before dragging her body outside and dumping it in the entry. For some reason, the killer took care to place the plate which Elizabeth had been given to carry the pork home, by her body.

This murder is strongly reminiscent of that of Madge Kirby, which took place in January 1908. The killer decoyed seven-year-old Madge away from a playing field off Kensington High Street with a promise of sweets, then raped and choked her at Number 15 Great Newton Street – a house that had lain empty for nine months. Madge's killer was described as a tall man with a dark moustache, just like the man who killed Elizabeth Peers. I feel there is a strong possibility that the killer of Madge and Elizabeth was one and the same man.

CAPTAIN MOONLIGHT

Aintree derives its name from the Anglo-Saxon 'an-treow' – meaning 'one tree' and that one tree was an ancient sprawling oak, sacred to the Druids and the Lily-White Boys cult of nature worshippers. This once heavily forested area is unusually flat, and when the trees of the great forest were cleared away, it became prime land for racing horses and pioneering aeroplane flights. In Elizabethan times, majestic horse races were held at Aintree and, of course, the place is synonymous today with the world-famous Grand National.

But let us now go back to the 1760s, when highwaymen such as Tom Barrow, Captain Moonlight, and Gentleman Higgins terrorised the good folk of Lancashire and Cheshire. Captain Moonlight was an unidentified highwayman, given his nickname by superstitious locals who believed him to be working in league with the Devil, as he always managed to avoid the law by apparently vanishing into thin air whenever he was on the point of capture. Tom Barrow, a rather effeminate-looking scoundrel, was said to have been taken prisoner in Maghull, where a bounty-hunter eventually discovered Barrow to be a Lord's beautiful daughter in disguise. Gentleman Higgins was a highwayman by night and a respectable member of the landed gentry by day, but someone finally put two and two together and Higgins was brought to justice, which in those days, meant execution. He ended up swinging from the gallows in 1767 before an assembled ring of well-to-do female spectators who had ghoulishly gathered together to watch the handsome rogue die.

The odd one out amongst these bandits of the road was Captain Moonlight, who was, without a doubt, also involved in Occultism. He was at large across a large swathe of Lancashire – from Hunt's Cross to Aintree – and was also active over an impossibly long time-span, unless, of course, someone else took on his mantle when he retired and nobody noticed the difference.

One night, on Tithe Barn Lane in Melling, Captain Moonlight held up a coach carrying a corrupt local magistrate and three of a local farmer's daughters who were regularly forced to be his mistresses. With two flintlocks trained on the magistrate and the driver, Moonlight ordered the Justice of the Peace to strip naked, and quaking with fear, he complied. The mysterious highwayman then proceeded to take what he considered to be his rightful share of the jewellery and items of value which the magistrate had secreted about his person. As he stuffed the booty into his saddlebags, he leant close to the magistrate and whispered with a smirk the word 'Meadows'. Those watching said that the magistrate took a step backwards and trembled anew. He stared at the robber in shock; obviously the word held some deep significance for him; it had definitely hit a raw nerve.

"Yes, I know your little secret, you rogue," said Moonlight, "and so shall everyone else unless you cease bothering these girls."

He then instructed the driver to take the farmer's daughters home, leaving the judge shivering naked in the road. Moonlight then spurred his horse and galloped off into the night.

Just exactly what Moonlight had meant by the word 'Meadows' has never been unravelled. Some speculated as to whether the magistrate had murdered an old landowner of that name years before, but no one really had the faintest idea. Armed possees of men scoured the length and breadth of Lancashire and beyond in an attempt to capture Captain Moonlight. At times they would catch a glimpse of the elusive highwayman, but he seemed to enjoy playing cat and mouse games with his pursuers, and just when they thought they had finally got him cornered, he would always vanish back into the night.

On one dark and foggy night he took the game one step further by placing a scarecrow on a horse. He had taken great pains to bedeck the scarecrow in identical clothes to his own usual attire and the posse chased after it as far as Kirkby, before they realised that they had been duped.

Almost a hundred years later, the people of Wavertree, West Derby and Old Swan were once more terrorised by a masked, cloaked man in a tricorn hat, who was believed by the superstitious amongst them to be Captain Moonlight. Some asserted that he could be nothing more than an impostor, but the older folks who had heard tales of him as children, were convinced that it was Moonlight, and that he had returned from Hell to indulge in his demonic pastime once again. Innocent women were allegedly outraged on their way to church, and every unexplained blaze in the districts where Moonlight was said to be at large, was accredited to him.

So who exactly was Captain Moonlight? Well, when I delved into the many accounts of the adventures of this sinister yet in some ways fair highwayman, a certain name cropped up again and again with a curious regularity, but no one would have suspected this person at the time, because he was a man of the cloth, but I cannot prove conclusively that he was the Highwayman from Hell. Yet this still leaves me with the problem of how can I explain his abnormally long life, which easily surpassed a hundred years, at a time when the normal life expectancy for a man was less than half of what it is today? Such longevity, coupled with that type of enduring agility, is impossible, unless he had struck a deal with someone who trades in souls …

HAUNTED HOSPITALS

When we pause to consider the number of patients who pass away in our hospitals every day, we should not be too surprised at the plethora of ghosts which are reported in them. Such places, where life-or-death dramas are acted out on a daily basis, are bound to harbour their fair share of ghosts, but not all the phantoms which are encountered within the walls of hospitals are those of former patients.

For many years, a ghostly woman, described as "nun-like" by a high proportion of those who saw her, was glimpsed for decades at the former Women's Hospital on Catharine Street. The ghost was seen mainly on the Duchess Ward, but also in other areas of the hospital. One sixty-seven-year-old woman at the hospital was so gravely ill that she was not expected to see the dawn of the next day, and was moved into a private room after receiving the Last Rites from the Roman Catholic chaplin.

During the early hours of the morning, the patient awakened in a confused state, partly because of sedation and partly because of her dire condition. As she slowly came to her senses, she noticed the silhouette of someone sitting at her bedside and initially thought it was her daughter. The figure stood up and leaned over the severely ill woman, and she could then see that she was a nun, of about forty-five to fifty years of age, with a face that radiated warmth and kindness. The nun held the patient's hands and after allaying the woman's fears with a soothing compassionate voice, she began to recite an old prayer that she hadn't heard since her schooldays.

The nun stayed with the woman throughout that long night, but vanished into thin air as the silver light of a summer dawn filtered through the blinds into the room, but before she disappeared, she whispered, "When you have to go one day, remember to have a happy death, because I promise you, you will meet loved ones who are waiting for you when you leave this part of life."

The next morning, the nurse coming on duty was astounded to find the patient sitting up in bed with a smile on her face; she had expected the bed to be empty, the woman having died in the night. In a strong voice, she told the nurse that her appetite had returned with a vengeance and she proceeded to eat a breakfast of porridge oats and toast and tea. That patient was discharged a mere two days later and lived for another fifteen years.

The 'phantom visitor' features regularly in many supernatural tales about hospitals, and what's more, I myself have had a personal experience of this phenomenon.

In 1990, when my mother was seriously ill in Clatterbridge Hospital, I travelled over to see her one afternoon and learned from one of the nurses that I had just missed my sister. At first, I presumed that she was talking about my sister who lived in Liverpool, but when I described her to the nurse as a petite blonde, the nurse returned a puzzled look. The woman she described had jet-black hair and was quite tall. I knew it couldn't be my eldest sister, as she has light brown hair and lived in Surrey. I asked my mother, who, though seriously ill, was fully conscious, if she could remember a young woman visiting her, and she said that a young woman of about twenty years of age had indeed visited her that afternoon.

"She was so kind," was all my mother could be persuaded to say about the mysterious visitor.

Each day when I turned up at Clatterbridge, I would learn from the nurses, or one of the doctors that I had again just missed my sister. They all remarked upon the blackness or her hair and the darkness of her eyes. Since I was the only person in my family with jet-black hair – I inherited my green eyes and black hair from my mother – I was puzzled to say the least. I telephoned my sisters and they told me that they hadn't a clue who this mysterious new 'sister' was. Whoever she was, she continued to visit my mother for a fortnight, and then was never seen or heard from again.

There have been several paranormal sightings reported at Clatterbridge Hospital over the years, in particular, one in which a man wearing a smart dark brown suit has been cited. This person is said to have visited patients in their sickbeds to comfort them with uplifting words. A misty image of a young woman with red hair has also been seen in the grounds of the hospital, and some believe she was once a conscientious nurse, who is still doing her duties, even after death. Now let us skim across the Mersey to investigate more of the haunted hospitals of Liverpool.

***

The foundation stone of the old Royal Infirmary on Pembroke Place was laid on 29 October 1887 by the Earl of Derby. The building, which incorporated Neo-Romanesque and Gothic architecture, took two years to build, and was designed by Alfred Waterhouse, an architect who had consulted many medical men and women (including Florence Nightingale) in the course of designing the hospital, to make sure that it met with all their requirements.

At a certain house that once existed on the site of the hospital, a ghostly woman in a wedding dress was often seen gazing morosely at the passers-by on Pembroke Place. The ghost was the apparition of a woman from Fairclough Street who had fallen from the upstairs window of her house on the day of her wedding, as a party was in progress downstairs. One person said that she had witnessed the whole thing and she insisted that the woman had fallen to her death accidentally. However, there were rumours that the new bride had, in fact, been pushed to her death by a jealous ex-lover, who somehow managed to infiltrate the wedding party and wreak his revenge on the happy couple.

The house was demolished soon after the tragedy, but the bridal ghost was still seen walking through Pembroke Place for some time afterwards. Even when the new Royal Infirmary was built on the site of the dead woman's home, her ghost continued to walk along the corridors of the new hospital, still dressed in a radiant white wedding gown and veil. Her ghost may also be responsible for the many sightings of the white lady of the 'old Royal' that were reported up until its closure in December 1978. The Royal Infirmary has so many strange tales – enough to easily fill a book this size. Here are just a selection of these supernatural incidents.

***

One rainy night in the mid-1960s, there was a frantic knocking at the door of a house in Kensington's Gilroy Street, the home of the Jones family. Mr Jones had put the bolt on the front door at midnight, and so, when the door-knocker sounded at 12.05am, he strictly forbade his daughters and wife to open the door. Mrs Jones was still curious, so she crept downstairs and peeped through the letterbox. Standing on the front step was Mrs Murphy, her friend who lived in nearby Tudor Street. Through the letter box Mrs Jones apologised for not being able to open the door because of her bully of a husband, and Mrs Murphy said, "Oh, that's alright, love. I've only come to say goodbye. You've been a great friend to me."

Mrs Jones was baffled by the strange remark, particularly at that late hour, but before she could ask Mrs Murphy why she was saying goodbye, the woman turned and walked off into the rainy night.

On the following morning, after Mr Jones had gone to work, his wife called at Mrs Murphy's home on Tudor Street, intending to get to the bottom of her friend's late-night call. When she arrived she was puzzled to find all the curtains drawn and was devastated to learn that Mrs Murphy had sadly passed away the night before at midnight, at the Royal Liverpool infirmary, from a brain haemorrhage. After getting over this initial shock, Mrs Jones suddenly realised the import of her friend's late night visit; she had come to say goodbye to her in spirit form.

I recall a surgeon who once told me how, one night in the 1960s, after a particularly long and difficult operation on a female patient, a woman in black appeared in the operating theatre wringing her hands in anxiety. "Oh thank you! Thank you!" she said to the surgeon – before vanishing into thin air. The surgeon was naturally startled by the ghost, and the patient whose life he had saved later told him that whilst under the general anaesthetic, she had seen her dead mother in a black dress in a dream – but a very realistic one – and she had been urging her not to worry because the surgeon was "very good".

In Edwardian times, the sinister apparition of a creeping shadow was seen by several patients at the Royal Infirmary, and I have documented one spine-chilling case concerning this entity in the tenth volume of *Haunted Liverpool*.

***

The David Lewis Northern Hospital, that stood between Great Howard Street and Leeds Street, had a variety of resident spooks, the oldest of which was said to be that of an old Jack Tar, who was often seen hurrying down a corridor in his clogs and typical mid-nineteenth century clothes. He would glance back with a look of intense fear on his blood-streaked face, as if he were being chased by someone out to kill him. The injured old sailor would continue to look back in terror as he rushed straight through a solid wall at the end of the corridor. This strange re-enactment took place with such regularity, that many of the nurses, doctors and medical staff became quite used to the ghostly replay.

In the 1960s, a pair of six-year-old red-headed twins died in a tragic traffic accident, and their autopsies were carried out at the hospital. During the routine examination to establish the cause of their deaths, a hospital porter and a nurse saw the ghosts of the twins playing happily in the corridor. The phantom children looked so utterly real, that the porter asked them where their mother and father were, upon which the identical youngsters just smiled and vanished.

***

At St Paul's Eye Hospital, in the 1970s, there were quite a few reports of a ghostly doctor with a distinct Northern Irish accent, who often singled out partially sighted patients and those patients recovering from surgery and spoke to them. He was an unusual ghost in that he apparently got himself around the city; an identical apparition was also seen in other hospitals over the years, including the Rathbone Hospital on Mill Lane, Old Swan, where he was said to have entered the building wearing a mackintosh and gauntlets of the type worn by motorcyclists in the 1920s. There were theories flying about at the time that the ghost was a former doctor, and there are further unfounded accounts of him being involved in a fatal motorcycle crash, but I have never been able to trace such a crash ... yet.

***

According to the many letters, emails and telephone calls I have received over the years, Whiston Hospital is one of the most haunted hospitals in the North West. One of the most intriguing apparitions which have manifested themselves around this hospital is that of a man dressed in what seems to be a monk's cowl. The apparition is of the 'carnate' class of ghost – that is, it looks completely solid – but no one has ever been able to give a satisfactory explanation as to what a monk is doing at Whiston Hospital, as there is no trace of any monastery in that area. All the same, the monk has been seen by so many people over the years, that it must have some very pressing reason for haunting the hospital.

In the course of my investigations into this entity, a nurse told me how she was coming off duty one evening, when she came across the hooded monk. He was standing eerily by the front gates of the hospital, like some silent sentinel. As she approached him, his solidity lessened, and he eventually became transparent before disappearing altogether. A security guard saw the same apparition that night, and on both occasions it slowly seemed to dissolve away, like a fade-out in a film, when it was approached.

Around the time of those sightings, a chapel that had stood for many years in the vicinity of the hospital was being demolished, and during that time there were many ghostly incidents reported. On one ward a ghostly grey figure of a man was seen to materialise twice in one evening, even sitting chumily on a patient's bed on each of the occasions. Strange sweet smells allegedly still invade parts of the hospital, and seem to precede such other worldly activities.

A phantom female nurse has also been seen occasionally walking through the surgical ward at Whiston Hospital, and she seems so real and even makes a noise as she walks, but she has the ability to disappear in a flash. Her identity remains a mystery. One nurse saw her ghostly counterpart during her break, and assumed that a new nurse had started at the hospital. She followed the newcomer into the staff kitchen, where she was astonished to see her fade into thin air. It has been alleged that there were so many ghost sightings in Ward K7, that it had to be blessed by a priest. That seemed to do the trick – the ghosts were laid to rest – but for how long?

***

In 1978, the shiny modern Royal Liverpool Teaching Hospital, on Prescot Street, first opened its doors to the public. One of the first ghosts to be seen on these premises was allegedly a woman in black, who was seen gliding in and out of an elevator at each of the eleven floors of the building, as if she were on castors. Originally she was regarded as an angel of death, as it was rumoured that she used to visit people who were on the point of death, but after researching this entity for many years, the reverse seems to be the case, and she really does seem to be more of an angel of mercy. Many of the patients she has visited have apparently made recoveries that are nothing short of miraculous.

A nurse who worked for many years at the Royal told me how she had seen the woman in black late one evening on Ward 9X. She was sitting at the bedside of a patient who had a severe medical condition and was not expected to live for more than a fortnight. The nurse mistook the ghost for a human visitor at first and was about to politely remind her that visiting hours had ended over an hour and a half ago, when she saw the pallid face of the 'visitor' and her odd-looking pale eyes which seemed to penetrate right into her soul. She backed away, and the ghost turned back to face the sleeping patient. That patient made a complete recovery over the next three days; a recovery that baffled the consultant in charge of her case.

The same ghost was seen by nurses and patients some weeks later walking silently from bed to bed on Ward 5Y. When one of the braver amongst them confronted the ghost, it seemed to transform itself into a two-dimensional image, before it evaporated before their eyes. The clothes which the apparition wore looked as if they dated from the 1930s.

Who is this ghost? or should I say, who was she in life? No one seems to have any idea.

***

The old Liverpool Maternity Hospital, on Oxford Street, opened in September 1926, and it provided the backdrop for many strange and supernatural goings-on, until its closure in the mid-1990s. Like many thousands of other Liverpudlians, I myself first saw the light of day at this hospital, and I was in good company, because so did John Lennon, who was born there in October 1940, allegedly during a World War Two air-raid.

In the 1950s, Gwen, a young Welsh nurse, worked at the Maternity Hospital for several years, and to her workmates, it soon became apparent that Gwen was highly psychic. She seemed to be able to sense whether a woman was going to have a miscarriage, a difficult birth, or a trouble-free one, and on several occasions she was able to see phantom people sitting at the bedsides of the pregnant women on the ward, when no one else could.

On one such occasion, Gwen noticed a blond-haired man sitting at the bedside of a young mother-to-be by the name of Janet, and before long she realised that he was a ghost. Gwen got talking to Janet, and learned that the girl had become pregnant by a young man called Terry who, soon after she found out she was pregnant, had tragically been killed in an accident on a building site. Struggling to stem the flow of tears that were welling up in her eyes, Janet showed the nurse a photograph of Terry. The photograph was

101

battered and worn, and was obviously looked at many times every day. Despite this, the young man was instantly recognisable as the same man who had been sitting at the girl's bedside. Gwen felt that Terry's love for his girlfriend had been so fervent that he had come back just to be with her for a while. When Janet gave birth to a baby daughter, Gwen again saw Terry's ghost watching over her and the new baby with a tear rolling down his cheek. Later that night, at about 10.30pm, when all the mothers and babies on the ward were asleep, she saw his ghost standing in utter desolation over the cot of his newborn child, as Janet slept, unaware of his presence.

Ever since the age of fourteen, Gwen had experienced vivid dreams in which she could clearly see every feature of her future husband's face, yet she didn't have a clue who he was. Imagine her surprise then when, one day, she was on duty at the hospital, and in walked a man with his heavily pregnant wife on his arm – and that man was the person she had repeatedly dreamt about for over ten years. Gwen was both amazed and saddened. Amazed because she felt as if she already knew the man – whose name was Robert – but saddened because he was married to someone else, and what's more, his wife was pregnant. The matron caught Gwen staring in disbelief at the husband and wife.

"Wake up, nurse!" she said sharply. "There isn't time to be standing around staring into space. Go and wash out the bedpans in the sluice."

"Yes, Matron. Sorry, Matron," said Gwen, hurrying towards the sluice. The last thing she wanted was to get on the wrong side of Matron, who had a fearsome reputation throughout the hospital.

As the young nurse went about her duties it was all she could do to stop herself from bursting into tears. She was so confused – normally her dreams were very accurate and she had fully believed that this individual would be her future husband; she knew his face better than any other living person. Gwen was so distracted by these thoughts of Robert that she felt she would explode. In the end she told another, older nurse, named Josie, about the situation. She had chosen Josie as a confidante because she believed in tea-leaf reading and dream interpretation, and was therefore quite open-minded towards the world of the supernatural. They had had many discussions about such matters over the years and she felt her advice would be invaluable.

Josie asked Gwen if she was absolutely sure that Robert was the man she had dreamed about for so long and Gwen assured her that he definitely was the man she had glimpsed so many times in her dreams over the years, and strangely enough, Robert certainly seemed to have noticed the lovely Welsh nurse. Upon first seeing her, he had smiled broadly at her and their eyes had locked, and when they got talking, he jokingly said that he had no intentions of being present at the birth.

A week later, Rob's wife gave birth to twins and she and her new babies and husband soon went home – a complete little family. However, a fortnight after that, Rob bumped into Gwen in Liverpool City Centre and immediately recognised her, despite the fact that she was out of uniform. Gwen wrestled to keep her emotions in check as he told her that his wife and the twins were doing fine and he praised the dedication and expertise of the hospital midwives and other medical staff.

Some weeks after that, he met Gwen by chance once again, this time on London Road, and joked, "We can't go on meeting like this". She had barely been able to answer or look at him, so overcome was she with emotion.

About seven months later, Robert turned up out of the blue at the Maternity Hospital one afternoon and asked the Matron specifically for Gwen, as he had something important to say to her. As it happened, Gwen was off sick that day, and Matron told Rob that she'd pass on the message to her when she returned to work, but Rob said that he'd rather see the girl in person, and so he came back to the hospital a week later.

Gwen was intrigued to know what it could possibly be that Rob had to tell her, and when he came up to the ward, she was at first shocked by what he told her – then ecstatic. Apparently, he had just found out that his wife had been having an affair, and she had admitted that the twins were not his. All babies are born with blue eyes and they either stay blue, or change to a different colour a few weeks after the birth. As the twins had grown, their eyes had changed from blue to brown, which had made Rob suspicious, because both he and his wife had blue eyes. His wife had turned cold towards him, which he had at first just put down to post-natal blues, but gradually the truth had dawned on him, and even before she admitted that she was having an affair, he had guessed the truth. They had now agreed to start divorce proceedings.

Gwen listened in silence to all this and then Robert said a curious thing. He revealed that from the first day that he had set eyes on Gwen, he had been unable to get her out of his mind. He had even dreamt about her on many occasions. They had been strong, realistic dreams, in which they were a loving couple. Rob was very concerned about what Gwen's reaction would be after hearing his story. He expected her to think that he was some kind of weirdo and he was convinced that she would tell him to clear off. Of course, nothing was further from Gwen's mind. She was unable to control her emotions a moment longer, and without any further discussion she hugged him, and they kissed.

Gwen later married Robert and gave birth to four of his children. She felt as if her dreams had literally come to pass.

WOLVES, HELL HOUNDS AND BIG CATS

One evening, in 2002, twenty-five-year-old Nicola was walking with Amber, her seven-year-old niece, from her mother's house in Halewood Green. There was a full moon just visible on the horizon, and Amber was walking alongside her mountain bike because the chain had come off and neither she nor Nicola knew how to fix it. They were walking down Okell Drive when they both heard a snarling noise coming from somewhere close by. It sounded as if some ferocious dog was running about off its leash but they couldn't quite make out exactly where the snarling was coming from. Then a massive creature bolted out of Trispen Close, leaving Amber hysterical and Nicola trembling in fear.

When they later described what they had seen and heard to a policeman, he thought they were winding him up, but aunt and niece were deadly serious. The thing they had seen looked like a huge wolf, they said, and it was at least twice as long as a German shepherd dog. The creature had bared a set of enormous yellow fangs, dripping with saliva, as it had snarled at Nicola and Amber, before galloping off at an incredible speed up Okell Drive towards Church Road.

A few days later, a similar wolf-like creature was seen on Gerrard's Lane, off Halewood Green by a couple walking from Clifton Avenue. One look at the animal's razor-sharp fangs sent them both running for home at breakneck speed. As they put some distance between themselves and the fearsome animal, it let out a bloodcurdling howl, like something out of a horror movie.

Another reported sighting of this same wolf-like creature was then made on Yew Tree Road, in November 2002, by an elderly woman. She initially thought that the animal was an Akita Ken breed of Japanese dog, but as it slunk along the road it crouched down low, as if ready to pounce, just like a wolf, and when viewed from side on, its body looked as if it was about seven feet in length.

Five years later, on 18 January 2007, I received an email from a woman who claimed to have seen an animal that she described as being like a "huge wolf" loping through Sefton Park, at around 4.30pm, just as it was going dark. The animal spun round when the woman's dog started barking at it. It paused for a few moments, as if trying decide whether or not to attack, and then sloped off.

On 20 January I received another report of a wolf sighting from a Mike Prescott, telling me how his children had run home, scared out of their wits, claiming that a wolf had chased them down Greenbank Drive (quite close to Sefton Park) at 5pm. The children said the wolf's eyes were an angry red, and its coat was a dark grey. Mr Prescott jumped in his car, leaving the children with his wife, and drove along Greenbank Drive to see for himself what his children had seen. He soon came across the animal – which he said was as big as a great dane, "sauntering casually" up Croxteth Drive, until it suddenly dashed off and he lost sight of it.

Not long after this sighting there were stories of a wolf at large on Gainsborough Road, Wavertree, and one woman in this area claimed to have had a chilling encounter with the out-of-place animal. The woman, named Pauline, was washing her hair in her flat on Bishopgate Street at 10 o'clock, when she heard a loud scratching sound at her front door. Thinking it was her dog Alfie wanting to come in, she went downstairs with her head wrapped in a towel and opened the front door.

"Come on, hurry …," Pauline stopped, mid-sentence, because she looked out into the street and could see no sign of her dog anywhere. Slightly perplexed, she closed the door and began to rub her hair dry with the towel as she walked into the front parlour. She was just about to switch on the lamp, when she saw a great, slavering animal's face staring at her through the bay window. It looked just like a wolf, with its glinting red eyes and its massive tongue lolling out of the side of its mouth.

Pauline panicked and began to back away towards the parlour door and stumbled in a confused state into the hallway. The creature then started to snap and snarl outside and then to hurl itself with full force at the front door. Pauline was convinced that at any minute the beast was going to burst the door off its hinges. She snatched her bag from off the bottom of the banister and pulled out her mobile phone. With trembling hands, she selected the number of her ex-boyfriend and told him what was happening. He drove straight round to her home, and although he didn't actually see the 'wolf', he couldn't question what had happened, because the deep jagged claw-marks were all too evident in the front door.

These reports may seem rather far-fetched, for how could an overgrown wolf possibly be at large in a built-up city such as Liverpool, without being seen all the time by hundreds of people? However, in 2007, Merseyside Police released documents to the public showing how, over a six-year period, they had received reports of panthers, lions, leopards and other beasts roaming the streets of the city. The statistics, released by the police under the Freedom of Information Act, are truly baffling. In that time period, Merseyside Police officers were called out to attend twenty-five incidents involving reports of dangerous animals.

One of the most bizarre reports dates from June 2006, when a six foot long creature, described as a panther, was seen prowling along the Loopline, a disused railway line that links Knowsley to Sefton. Then, in July of the same year, a terrified woman in Croxteth called the police to report sightings of lions and tigers in the road. Other residents also saw these fearsome animals, but were naturally at a loss to understand where they had come from. Equally mystifying was a report in September 2006 of a panther darting between the rocks on Egremont promenade, in Liscard.

On the other side of the Mersey, at Southport, two huge lions were reported to the police as they roamed around Mill Lane. They carried out an investigation but could find no trace of the big cats. No zoos were missing any of their animals at the time either. A surreal report logged by the police states that a patrol car was requested after a puma was seen wandering about on the thirteenth hole of Wirral Ladies Golf Club at Bidston Road, Oxton. Police were naturally sceptical about the report, until they found a series of massive paw prints criss-crossing the green. Around the time of the panther reports, the Halewood Wolf was seen again near a caravan park on Lower Road, ambling alongside Ditton Brook. That same week, a large wolf (perhaps the same one as that seen at Halewood) was seen under curious circumstances.

Two men in their fifties, Jim Gower and John Banks, were drinking in the Black Horse Inn at Cronton, Widnes, when they met an old friend by the name of Frank Parker. Frank was in sombre mood and was reflecting on how physical decline was inevitable as a person grew older, but Jim and John disagreed, and said that they could still do most of the things that they had done when they were eighteen. Frank reminded the duo how, in their teens, they had regularly walked ten miles to court two girls who lived in Knotty Ash.

"Bet you couldn't do that now," he said.

"Don't talk so daft," said fifty-six-year-old John Banks. "I could easily walk to Knotty Ash from Widnes. Ten miles is nothing for a man in my condition."

"Yeah! Course you can," said fifty-seven-year-old Jim Gower. "Nothing to it. In fact, I bet I could do it in less three hours."

"Oh you could, could you?" said Frank Parker. "Well, I'll bet you twenty quid that neither of you can do it."

"You're on!" said the two other men in unison, and so they shook hands and accepted Frank's wager.

The next day at noon they set out from the Black Horse Inn, bound for The Wheatsheaf public house, on East Prescot Road, Knotty Ash. Frank Parker told the men that if he found any evidence of them using transport of any kind, the wager would be annulled immediately.

"What'd you take us for?" said John Banks, indignantly. "Come on, Jim, let's show him."

The two men, dressed for the occasion in tracksuits and trainers, set off at a brisk pace, relishing the challenge. They got as far as Dacre's Bridge Lane near Junction 6 of the M62, when they stopped in their tracks. A long grey animal resembling a wolf was loping diagonally across a field at the side of the road. Both men froze upon realising the sheer size of the animal – they had never seen anything like it before. fortunately it was moving away from them and they watched it trot off towards Tarbock Hall in the distance. The strange sighting gave them plenty to talk about for the rest of their trek to Knotty Ash, making the time pass quickly. They arrived at the Wheatsheaf pub at 3.20pm, where Frank Parker paid his friends twenty pounds each, even though they had taken more than three hours to walk the distance.

Where do these out-of-place animals come from and how do they manage to feed themselves without being discovered? The problem has been mooted before, whenever reports of the Surrey Puma, or the Beast of Bodmin arise. A colony of panthers, or even a single wolf of the type reported around Liverpool and its suburbs would need to slaughter a sizeable number of farm animals with regularity to survive, yet this doesn't seem to be the case. Could it be possible that these animals come from another dimension that runs alongside ours? If not, then surely when these animals died – as they would have to do at one stage in their lives, if they were made of flesh and blood – they would leave their carcasses and bones behind, yet no such remains have ever been found.

This lack of tangible evidence leads me to lean towards a more supernatural interpretation; that these creatures somehow enter our time period from somewhere else, and the phenomenon seems to have been going on for quite some time now. The enigmatic Surrey puma has been seen since at least 1770 and the equally sinister black dogs that haunt Lancashire, Cheshire and most of the counties of Britain, date back even further. The black hound that haunts Crosby's waterfront is thought to date back over a thousand years, and was always regarded as a shape-shifting demon dog.

One evening, in the 1950s, a widowed woman, Nelly McGloughlin, was passing the Congregational Church (now known as 'The Blackie') on Great George Street, when she became aware that she was being followed by a hound that resembled an enormous black Great Dane. Mrs McGloughlin hurried along Stanhope Street to her house, and was relieved when she got to her door and looked around to find that the huge dog had gone. The street was unusually deserted, save for a few cars passing by, and Mrs McGloughlin sensed that there had been something evil about the dog.

The widow entered her home and was greeted by her seventeen-year-old daughter Carol in the hallway. Carol was already in her pyjamas and headed up the stairs to bed, saying goodnight with a yawn as she did so. About forty minutes later, after making herself a bit of supper, Mrs McGloughlin climbed the stairs to her own bedroom. She opened the bedroom door, and was about to switch on the light, when a shocking sight rooted her to the spot. The colossal black dog that she had seen earlier near the church was straddling her double bed, its gangly limbs dangling over either side of the duvet. It was gazing at the frightened widow with red glowing eyes. Its mouth was opened slightly and seemed to grin in an almost human way.

Mrs McGloughlin slammed the door on the canine beast and ran across the landing and into her daughter's room. For over an hour mother and daughter remained huddled together in that room, the door barricaded with a sideboard against the evil-looking red-eyed hound. Then, hearing footsteps, Carol opened the window and saw her neighbour, a tall docker named Mr Davy, coming back from the pub. Trying to keep the panic out of her voice, she told him about the huge dog with the strange eyes, but he didn't know what to make of the story.

"Hysterical women!" Davy thought to himself. "It's usually spiders, or mice. Massive dogs is definitely a new one."

However, when Carol threw down her keys and begged him to help her and her mum, he had no choice but to enter the house and try and find out what all the fuss was about. The docker opened the door and stepped into the darkened hallway. He investigated all the rooms, one at a time, beginning with those downstairs. He found no raven-black Great Dane, with dripping jaws – just two terrified women, cowering in one of the bedrooms. It took him quite a while to convince them that there was nothing sinister in any of the rooms, and after sharing a cup of tea with them, he finally went home, where he and his wife had a laugh about the whole incident.

Nelly, however, was in no doubt about what she had seen, and about a month later, she saw the same giant black dog one night on Upper Parliament Street, but she was glad that, on this occasion, several other people in the street also saw the fearsome-looking canine. It came bounding towards Nelly, and she and two other bystanders scrambled up the steps to the nearest house and hammered on the door. When the owner answered it, they barged past him, with no explanation, and shot into the back of the house to hide.

The hound was occasionally seen again in Toxteth over the years, and would always seem to appear out of thin air at the top of the steps of the Congregational Church on Great George Street. Like all of the reports of out-of-place animals mentioned in this section, the black dog of Toxteth is exceedingly difficult to explain away.

THE CHRISTMAS TREE

The real green Christmas tree, with its delicious seasonal aroma of pine, sparkled with tinsel and was all aglow with a myriad of blue, red, pink, amber and green lights.

"That's very clever," John Clarke thought to himself, "electric lights!"

The fairy at the top of the tree was the work of John's six-year-old sister, Joan. The little girl had carefully wrapped her smallest doll in yellow crepe paper, then glued wings of coloured cellophane to its back, and fashioned the fairy wand from a matchstick and a tiny cut-out silver foil star. Now John surveyed the family tree and closed his eyes in wondrous contemplation; how beautiful it was, how safe and warm, not to be alone at this time of the year, but to have a family ...

Not so long ago he had been without anyone to love him, an outcast from society, but now it was Christmas Eve and here he was, imagining himself once again in the bosom of his family. Goosefeather-sized snowflakes fluttered erratically from the clouds drifting low across the sapphire-blue night sky, and everywhere, excited children were climbing the stairs eagerly thinking about the old man in scarlet and the gifts he would leave for them, wrapped in the holly and ivy patterned wrapping paper, and sealed with red tape. On this, the most exciting night of the year, you could almost feel the magical expectations hanging in the night air.

John Clarke turned towards the fireplace, the centre of the home, with his sister's stocking hanging from the mantelpiece and the note to Santa Claus resting against the old clock. In the kitchen, the wicker-basket hamper was open and ready to feed the family, and the Christmas pudding lay in a covered pan on the hob, ready to be boiled for hours in the morning, filling the house with steam. Chestnuts and tangerines, turkey and Christmas crackers – and, of course, the little birthday cake for Joan. You see, Joan had been born on Boxing Day six years ago, and had almost died. With a deep sigh, the doctor had held his stethoscope to the tiny scrap's chest and listened gravely. He then turned to her mother and said, "Nothing I can do for her, I'm afraid, Mrs Clarke. You'd better get her baptised while there's still time."

111

Mrs Clarke refused to accept the doctor's dark forebodings, but how could she hang on to her precious little girl? Joan was too weak to be breast-fed, and no one could work out how the gravely ill baby could take the nourishment that she so desperately needed to survive, but her big brother John suddenly had an idea. He diligently cleaned out a fountain-pen filler with boiling water and then suggested to his grandad that if he filled it with milk, they could put it into his baby sister's tiny mouth and try and feed her. John's parents dismissed the idea as being crazy at first, but as the baby became weaker and weaker they could see her literally slipping away before their eyes, they decided that anything was worth a try. John's grandfather had also added a tear-drop-sized amount of brandy into the fountain-pen filler – and whether it was this, or the milk, it was an instant success. Little Joan began to revive immediately and gradually made a recovery over the following days and weeks.

The girl grew to be healthy and strong and never tired of this story – how big brother John had saved her with his brilliant idea – and she would act out the scene, putting a pen to her doll's mouth and pretending to make her drink.

Then one day Joan said to her brother, "If I had died, would I have gone to sleep forever?"

She thought John knew the answers to everything.

"You would have just not known anything," replied John. "You'd be all alone as well, and you'd never see me, or mummy or daddy again, and then we'd have forgotten all about you."

Joan was frightened by his rather stark reply, and started to cry. John hugged her and said, "But you're alive now, so don't worry, and you'll always be alive, I'll make sure of that."

The little girl sniffled and said, "I don't ever want to die. I want to live forever and stay here with you and mummy and daddy."

And, of course, all that was many years ago, before John's whole family had been wiped out in the Blitz. As he remembered that terrible night – the screams, the smells, the rubble … and the bodies of the people he loved most in the world – the image of the old house faded away around him. Only the twinkling Christmas tree remained – but it wasn't his. It stood in the window of a shop on Bold Street. The people passing by didn't even notice the old tramp's tears as he trundled off into the night, surrounded by so many happy smiling people, yet so alone again.

JUDDA THE EVERTON LEPRACHAUN

There was a bizarre case of an alleged leprechaun being used by housebreakers to gain entry to various premises in the early 1890s. A boy named Billy Gunnion, living on Stanley Road in Everton, came home one April afternoon in 1892, soaked to the skin from a sudden downpour, and with him there was someone who was initially taken to be a child – until the lad's mother looked more closely. If indeed he was a child, he was a very strange looking one, because he had the face of a man in his fifties. Mrs Gunnion was naturally startled and a little scared by the man, who measured about two-and-a-half feet in height. She asked him who he was, and he returned a puzzled look, then began to speak in what sounded like the Gaelic tongue. Mrs Gunnion asked her son why he had brought the 'midget' as she rudely referred to him, to their home. Young Billy said that he had noticed him walking with his head bowed down as he walked along Stanley Road. He had looked so sad and was soaked to the bone from the heavy rain. Billy's instincts had prompted him to invite the little man home and to treat him to a hot cup of tea in front of a blazing fire.

Billy's mother was furious at her son's act of charity, and was about to throw the little man out, until Mr Gunnion came into the parlour to see what all the fuss was about. He knew a little Gaelic from his grandmother, and so he attempted to converse with the pint-sized visitor. What he learned was truly stunning. The strange dwarf claimed to be a leprechaun from County Kerry, in southern Ireland. His name was Judda and he had travelled as a stowaway on a ship that had sailed from Cork to Liverpool. Mrs Gunnion made the sign of the cross when she heard this, then slapped the back of Billy's head.

"Oh! Jesus, Mary and Joseph!" she said. "You're as bad as the lad himself. Will you get rid of that leprechaun at once. I don't want him anywhere near my house. Get him out."

"Will you calm down, Missus," said her husband, shaking his head. "The lad was only doing his Christian duty, and anyway, we'll have great luck if we show the little fella some hospitality."

A great row then ensued between Mr and Mrs Gunnion, while Billy and Judda looked on, embarrassed. However, the upshot of it was that Judda was finally allowed to stay in the back parlour for a few days, as long as he kept out of Mrs Gunnion's way.

Mr Gunnion and his brother-in-law, Eddy Durham, who lived locally, were both burglars, and they were quick to see the benefits of having a thirty-inch-tall man at their disposal. He would be able to squeeze into places that neither of them could normally even consider getting into.

One night, Judda was taken to the premises of a wealthy joiner and builder by the name of Worthington, on Roscommon Street. In the backyard of Worthington's home there was a ground-floor sash window that could only be opened six inches. This window was skilfully prised open, and Judda was shoved through the narrow gap. In Gaelic he had been given basic instructions to steal anything of value in the house, and fifteen minutes after entering the house, Judda returned to the window carrying a gold watch, a pair of brass candlesticks and a purse packed with money. This was to be the first of several such burglaries, in which a normal-sized human could not have gained access to the house, but that Judda was able to enter easily.

Unfortunately, Judda was attacked by a dog one night during one of these illegal escapades, just minutes after slipping into a house on William Henry Street. Polly Smith, a huge woman who lived alone at the house with her dog Kelly, hit the leprechaun over the head with a bed-warming pan, knocking him clean out. Police later took the hapless Judda into custody and tried to interrogate him. It finally occurred to one of the brighter officers amongst them, that their little burglar spoke only Gaelic, and a translator was sent for.

Judda's claim to be an Irish leprechaun was not entertained by the police, who assumed that he was nothing more than a dwarf who was trying to masquerade as a leprechaun in order to save his skin. Judda had no reason to protect the two burglars. After all, it was they who had got him into this mess in the first place. So he told the authorities where his accomplices lived, and within no time Messrs Gunnion and Durham were being quizzed at the police station about their whereabouts on the night of the William Henry Street break-in. Both men were tried and found guilty of the crime and were sentenced to a term of imprisonment, whilst Judda apparently ended up in the workhouse.

If you find any of this hard to believe, then here are two articles from the Liverpool Courier, dated 13 and 14 August 1908.

IRISH LEPRECHAUN CAPTURED
Refuses to Be Interviewed

The Central News Mullingar correspondent telegraphs that a great sensation has been caused in Mullingar by the report that the Leprechaun, which several children stated they had seen at Killough, near Delvin, during the past two months,was captured last night.

Two policemen found a creature of dwarfish proportions in a wood near the town, and brought the little man to Mullingar Workhouse, where he is now an inmate. He eats greedily, but all attempts to interview him have failed, his only reply being a peculiar sound between a growl and a squeal.

And here is the follow-up to this amazing story:

THE CAPTURED LEPRECHAUN
Eats, Drinks and Smokes

The reported capture of the Killough leprechaun continues to cause considerable sensation in Mullingar. When seen by a correspondent yesterday, he was seated on a bench in the infirm ward of the workhouse, and in reply to questions, made little more than strange jabbering sounds, very occasionally uttering a coherent word or two, from which it was gathered that he claims County Down as his native place, and that he was in County Meath prior to his appearance in the woods near Mullingar, where he was found by the police. He has a very knowing expression of face, sometimes grave and sometimes lighted up with a grin. Standing not more than four feet high, the mannikin altogether looked a strange little creature. His most striking characteristic is the avidity with which he eats and drinks. He also smokes a pipe.

The fate of the 'leprechaun' is unknown.

AGENTS OF THE EVIL GENIUS?

Does something truly evil, with the sole purpose of trying to persuade everyday people to kill and commit acts of malevolence, really exist under the streets of Liverpool? I know an Occultist who believes that the thing to which I am referring is one of the many Fallen Angels, rumoured to be sleeping, or lurking in the bowels of the earth, whereas another investigator of the paranormal thinks the being is actually crystallised hatred, with as much reality and consciousness as the earth's magnetic field. Unfortunately, these interpretations are of little use to me as a chronicler of paranormal Liverpool. All I can do is describe the events as they happened in the accounts I have heard and try and make sense of them.

A few years ago there was a stabbing incident in Liverpool city centre, and the man who was wielding the knife was known to his friends and family as a calm, mild-mannered individual, who never even raised his voice in anger, never mind used a blade. Yet this man was walking innocently down Fenwick Street one night when he found a knife lying on the ground. For some inexplicable reason, he found himself bending down and picking up that knife and then plunging it into his friend of many years, missing one of his vital organs by a fraction of a centimetre.

When questioned afterwards, he insisted that he had no idea why he had stabbed his friend, but at the time he remembered feeling an incredible wicked urge to do it. At the same moment as the attacker was overpowered by the urge to carry out this senseless act of violence, he felt something cold rise up from his feet and course up through both his legs simultaneously. The icy chill rose on up through his abdomen and ribcage, chilling his heart, before coursing upwards through his neck, until it reached his brain, numbing all his senses. Then he saw the fabled 'red mist' which soldiers describe when they are in the thick of battle, when the mind is filled with an overwhelming urge to kill. After the attack, that peculiar coldness flowed back down the assailant's body, down into his legs, into his ankles, and down into the soles of his feet in their shoes – as if it had gone back into the ground like an earthed electrical charge.

In another incident, two girls in their early twenties who had been the best of friends since they were at infant school, were walking past the Slaughterhouse Pub on Fenwick Street one night, when they both started insulting one another. For no apparent reason, they were suddenly at one another's throats, and luckily, the police were on hand to separate the girls and calm the situation down. They later contacted me and told me how they had both felt at the time. They said that it was as if they had been simultaneously possessed by something evil as they walked down the street. The girls were both very upset when they got home and tended to the scratches on one another's faces, and compared notes on what had provoked the uncharacteristic behaviour. It was very strange, because they had both felt as if something cold and evil had 'slid' inside of their bodies earlier that evening, and they suffered nightmares about it for weeks afterwards.

Unfortunately, this is a scenario which I have heard again and again, and it leads me to believe that some abomination, capable of possessing the minds of certain people, is at large under the streets of the city centre, in a specific area that stretches from Slater Street to Water Street. The sceptic would argue that drink and drugs are more likely to be responsible for these acts of motiveless violence, rather than some malevolent metaphysical force, but the alcohol and narcotics theory doesn't really fit the facts. I am talking about cases where the person afflicted feels possessed, has no control over himself or herself, and has no cause or stimulus to be violent.

***

An off-duty bouncer told me how one summer evening he was coming out of the Jacaranda pub on Slater Street with a friend when he suddenly felt a strange freezing cold sensation enter his head via a spot under his left ear, just below the jawline. The bouncer was alarmed by the unpleasant sensation of creeping coldness as it spread up the side of his head, causing numbness in the left half of his face. He naturally assumed he was suffering some kind of stroke, but soon realised that something much stranger and even more sinister was taking place. The bouncer began to be bombarded by intensely vile thoughts which raced out of control in his head. He broke out in a sweat, and when his friend asked him if he was feeling alright, the bouncer found a tremendous anger swelling up inside himself, and he suddenly felt a powerful and irresistible urge to strike out at his companion.

The bouncer's friend, meanwhile, noticed something quite bizarre. The bouncer's eyes seemed faintly luminous. The bouncer then experienced the very same sensations described by the man who stabbed his friend in Fenwick Street. He shivered as something ice-cold passed from his neck, down his backbone, into his left leg, and into his foot. He felt dizzy and weak, and was left feeling quite confused by the glacially cold 'thing' that had moved down through his body. Later that evening, after he had recovered his equilibrium, the bouncer set off for a quiet pub in the suburbs of Liverpool, to collect his thoughts. He bought a pint and was supping it quietly, mulling over the strange events of the past couple of hours, when he noticed an old woman sitting by herself in a corner of the bar who kept looking at him intently. The bouncer felt distinctly uncomfortable under this elderly woman's constant gaze, and after finishing his pint, got up, ready to go home, when she suddenly came over to him and said a curious thing.

"Start going to church, love," she told him. The bouncer returned a puzzled look, but the woman continued, "There is something very nasty out to get your soul. You might think I'm potty, son, but I have a gift … I know."

Normally the bouncer would have turned his back on anybody who had approached him in such a way, but in the light of the strange incident that had taken place on Slater Street, her words hit a chord and he listened, intrigued. The woman told him that the world was becoming infested with evil beings that were invisible and almost undetectable to the average person. They detested light and truth, and secreted themselves under the ground during the day. They could invade a person's body and lie dormant, waiting for the right opportunity to do evil, or they could instantly influence a person to carry out heinous acts of hate.

The woman then referred to the recent shocking murder of five children at an Amish school in Pennsylvania, in the United States, and hinted that such a possession had been the cause of that tragedy. On the morning of 2 October, 2006, Charles Carl Roberts, a thirty-two-year-old family man with no history of violence, had entered the one-roomed Amish schoolhouse and taken the schoolchildren hostage. In an arbitrary act of savagery, Roberts ordered five of the hostages – their ages ranging from seven to thirteen – to line up against the chalkboard, and shot all five of them dead at point blank range. To this day, no one has been able to discover any motive for this atrocity, and it would seem that

Roberts had never shown any violent tendencies before.

The bouncer remembered the incident vividly, and he instantly felt the wisdom of the old woman's words. He started to attend church and slowly his life underwent a positive change. He came to be convinced that the old woman in the pub was right; there really were evil things at large in this world, and he had been lucky to have experienced them and escape unharmed.

The reports of the ice-cold invasive mind-altering 'thing' continue to come in, and an ex-Satanist named Stephen believes that we are dealing with ancient demons who were thrown down on to the earth thousands of years ago after the War in Heaven between the Angels of God and the Angels of the cherub Lucifer. The cause of this unimaginably terrifying conflict was God's orders to his angels to bow to mankind. Lucifer was outraged by the command and refused to carry it out. He amassed a following of 133,306,668 angels, and they battled 266 million angels loyal to God. God's angels won this war on high, and Lucifer and his surviving angels were thrown 'like lightning' down on to the earth, where they dwelt underground, stripped of most of their powers.

Since then, Occultists have given many names to these cast-down angels. Some call them demons, others the Ancient Ones, the Luciferians, the Fallen Angels and so on. Some believe that there is nothing short of a Satanic revival going on in the world today, with the global crime rate soaring, wars raging, widespread extreme acts of terrorism, and genocidal massacres coming to light. I sometimes wonder whether there is some evil genius, some unseen malevolent force that has been responsible for every war and atrocity that has ever been waged on this planet, from the Battle of Crécy to the latest conflicts going on all over the globe today.

Stephen, a person who was once involved in a dark Satanic cult, believes that people have to get back to believing in the power of good and the positive in order to be able to combat this evil force. He advises people to always wear a talisman, or symbol of their faith, be it the Star of David, a crucifix, an Ankh – whatever symbolises their particular faith. When things like racism, egotism, ageism and sexism raise their ugly heads, we should realise that it may not be simple human emotion or mistaken beliefs in action, but agents of the evil genius at work, goading us on to generate even more negativity in a world already swamped with violence and hatred.

THE DIAMOND BULLET

In autumn 1896, the Three Wise Monkeys, who represent that ancient maxim – 'See no evil, hear no evil, speak no evil' – arrived in Liverpool, by a circuitous route from the Far East. The three Japanese porcelain figurines were in near perfect condition and would fetch a pretty penny at Christie's auction house, and their owner, fifty-eight-year-old millionaire James Hardy, knew that much already. He had hired the greatest experts and antique evaluators who specialised in Oriental porcelain to look at the pieces, and they had all told him that these three monkeys, named Swazaru, Mizaru and Kikazaru, belonged to the Edo period, and predated their life size replicas which are carved over the door of a seventeenth century Shinto shrine in Japan.

It was an unheard of prize in the world of antiques, for a collector to have acquired three two hundred-year-old figurines from Japan made by an obscure craftsman named Akunin. It seemed that these three monkeys were apparently unique, the only set of their kind in the world. Mr Hardy was fabulously rich anyway, and got his pleasure, not from the art itself, but from the possession of something which no one else had, and he seemed to feed off the jealousy of the other collectors with whom he was acquainted.

It is possible, therefore, to imagine the enormous shock he experienced, when the long arm of coincidence reached into Mr Hardy's life and introduced him, by a chance acquaintance at his gentleman's club, to a man who owned a single wise monkey made by the same master potter, Akunin? This man was Godfrey Hastings, a jeweller of Seymour Street. He had found the monkey – which held its hands over its mouth – in the possession of a cousin who had died twenty years before. Mr Hardy asked to see the monkey and immediately offered Hastings a hundred guineas for the porcelain figure, but the old jeweller kindly declined the offer, saying that the monkey was of sentimental value and he couldn't part with it, even for so generous a sum. "Then I'll give you three-hundred guineas," said Hardy, quaking with emotion, but the old man only held the monkey more tightly to his breast, and and stroked it, calling it an old friend. Ridiculous amounts of money were quoted repeatedly by Hardy, who only wanted the monkey so that he could destroy it to ensure that his Three Wise simians were unique in this world.

Plots to steal that monkey, and even to kill its owner were hatched, but discarded as ridiculous by James Hardy. He had to get that monkey off Hastings, and he needed an original idea. The pursuit of that porcelain monkey became an obsession which plagued him day and night.

One afternoon he bumped into his old friend Lieutenant-Colonel John Hall – who had a reputation for being one of the greatest crack-shots in the British Army at the time – and who was now stationed at the Sefton Barracks on Upper Warwick Street. Hall loved any kind of challenge or a dare, and Hardy offered him one that he couldn't resist.

"Would it be possible," he asked, " to shatter a porcelain figure resting on a mantelpiece in a parlour from two hundred feet away?"

"Yes, it would," replied Hall confidently. "Let the dog see the rabbit, old boy. Where is this bit of porcelain you're talking about anyway?"

"Oh, it's not far from here, at the house of a friend of mine," said Hardy. "Come on, I'll take you there and we can do a bit of reconnoitring."

And so the plot was hatched. To ensure that the monkey would be destroyed beyond repair, Hall suggested using a diamond-tipped bullet, and Hardy conjured up the funds to design such a projectile. Secretly, Hall thought that Hardy was barking mad, but he went along with the plan because he enjoyed all the intrigue and excitement.

And so, one week later, from the window of a rented house facing Godfrey Hastings' home, John Hall peered through his telescopic rifle sight and trained the cross-hairs on the monkey figurine, which rested on the mantelpiece, in pride of place. The room was only illuminated by two gas mantles, so he had to strain hard to focus on his target. Old Godfrey was sitting close to the hearth, reading – just out of the line of fire – completely unaware of the dastardly deed that was about to be perpetrated on him in the name of jealousy. Godfrey's safety did not concern Hardy in the least; he had nothing personal against him, in fact, by all accounts he was a pretty decent fellow. But he was so utterly consumed with his overriding obsession to destroy that monkey, that he was prepared to do it, no matter what the cost.

A deafening crack rang out. A window pane tinkled, and the porcelain figure shattered into powder. The job was done and the two men hastily beat a retreat from the rented house. Hall was paid a princely sum for his staggering marksmanship and James Hardy was able to sleep soundly once again.

Now comes the twist.

The antiques experts were wrong, for that month, sixty-five identical sets of the Three Wise Monkeys turned up at Christie's, all exactly the same as James Hardy's set. What's more, it turned out that they weren't centuries old, but a mere twenty years, and Akunin – a Japanese word for villain – was apparently still churning them out by the dozen every day.

THE THING FROM THE WARDROBE

As soon as the sun started going down, thirteen-year-old Nathan would stop playing his computer games and leave his bedroom in case he met the 'thing' from his wardrobe. Nathan's parents had told him repeatedly that he must be imagining things. His favourite teacher at school, an understanding woman named Beth, had listened sympathetically to his tales of persecution by a grotesque entity, and she had advised her pupil to sleep with the light on and to stop watching horror films late at night.

But nothing worked. Lights were left on and duct tape was used to seal the wardrobe door, but the thing would still force open the door most nights and terrorise the young teenager.

It had all started without warning in April 2006, at the very ordinary semi-detached house in a certain district of Liverpool. One evening, Nathan had been sitting on his bed, engrossed in a Playstation game, when the door of the wardrobe had creaked open a few inches. Nathan glanced over, and played on, but then the door continued to open steadily, so he paused the game and stared at the wardrobe with goosebumps rising up all over his body. At the same time, he had a strong sensation that something had just entered his bedroom. He closed the wardrobe door and went downstairs to get away from the atmosphere of fear. He told his mum about the incident and she joked, "Oh you must have a ghost in your room, Nathan. Come and watch telly with me and your dad. It's *Coronation Street*."

Nathan eventually went back to his room when he could no longer keep his eyes open to watch the television, at about 11pm. He got into bed and like most kids of that age, was sound asleep in seconds. However, at about four o'clock in the morning he was awakened by a stranger calling out his name. Nathan looked over at the wardrobe and its door was wide open again, but this time the interior was swirling with smoke. Within the smoke, a terrifying face with luminous eyes expanded from a small spot until it filled the whole of the inside of the wardrobe. The teenager ducked under the blankets feeling terrified and vulnerable, and seconds later, something ice-cold snatched at his left foot and painfully grabbed him by the ankle.

Nathan screamed, wrestled his foot from the icy grip and jumped out the bed. A dark oval mass of swirling mist, with a pair of staring eyes in the middle, hovered at the foot of the bed. This entity had four arm-like extensions with three long fingers at each end, and each of these arms made a grab at the teenager as he fled towards the door. Nathan ran into the bedroom of his older brother Liam and woke him up. Keeping his voice low, he whispered to Liam about the thing in his bedroom, and his brother grumpily told him to go back to bed after squinting at the clock and seeing the time – but then he heard strange laughter coming from Nathan's room and sat bolt upright.

Liam, a Marine Cadet, was afraid of nothing. He strode into Nathan's room and watched as the door of the wardrobe opened and closed of its own accord, but he saw nothing unusual inside it, just Nathan's clothes on their hangers and bits of his junk bundled in the bottom.

On the next occasion when the thing appeared, Liam was awakened by his screaming brother and he came flying into his room to find the ovoid-shaped being floating over the bed. Liam stood in front of Nathan and bravely squared up to the thing, and asked, "What are you? and why do you keep coming here and frightening my brother?"

The thing began to groan horribly and then to speak in an unknown language, but at that moment the boys' father entered the room, and switched on the light, which caused the entity to vanish. He asked why they had been making such a racket, but the teenagers just looked at each other and said nothing. They instinctively knew that their father would never believe what they had seen in a million years.

"Well, get back to bed then, the pair of you. Honestly! Waking me and your mother up at this time of night."

"Sorry, Dad," said Liam. "I think Nathan had a nightmare."

"Okay then. Let's all get some sleep."

As soon as their father had gone back to bed, the two boys discussed what they had seen, but they could make no sense of it. Liam bravely suggested that they should swap bedrooms, which is what they did, and since then, the thing from the wardrobe hasn't reappeared once.

To me, the thing is reminiscent of a demon, feeding on fear, but why on earth did it come from a wardrobe of all places? I had a look at the wardrobe in question and determined that it was made of acacia, a tough resinous hardwood that is naturally waterproof and does not stain. Such wood is held in high esteem in the Occult world and is alleged to have magical properties. The sacred container known as the Ark of the Covenant mentioned in the Old Testament, was made of acacia, and the Sprig of Acacia, symbolises the immortality of the soul in some of the older Masonic traditions. The most important aid in ritual magic is probably the magician's wand, and acacia was a favourite material of ancient magicians when they created their wands. I may be wildly wrong, but I had a strong feeling about the acacia wardrobe in Nathan's room. His mother said that it had belonged to her grandmother, and she had told her that it had belonged to her father before that, and he had brought it from India, where he had been stationed as a colonel. The wardrobe is certainly Victorian, but beyond that I feel it holds some dark secret. Perhaps in time the four-armed entity will return and if someone is brave enough to confront the being, and clever enough to understand its strange language, they will get to the bottom of this intriguing supernatural mystery.

OTHER TITLES BY TOM SLEMEN

HAUNTED LIVERPOOL 1	Tom Slemen	£5.99
HAUNTED LIVERPOOL 2	Tom Slemen	£5.99
HAUNTED LIVERPOOL 3	Tom Slemen	£5.99
HAUNTED LIVERPOOL 4	Tom Slemen	£5.99
HAUNTED LIVERPOOL 5	Tom Slemen	£5.99
HAUNTED LIVERPOOL 6	Tom Slemen	£5.99
HAUNTED LIVERPOOL 7	Tom Slemen	£5.99
HAUNTED LIVERPOOL 8	Tom Slemen	£5.99
HAUNTED LIVERPOOL 9	Tom Slemen	£5.99
HAUNTED LIVERPOOL 10	Tom Slemen	£5.99
HAUNTED LIVERPOOL 11	Tom Slemen	£5.99
HAUNTED LIVERPOOL 12	Tom Slemen	£5.99
HAUNTED LIVERPOOL 13	Tom Slemen	£5.99
STRANGE LIVERPOOL	Tom Slemen	£5.99
HAUNTED WIRRAL	Tom Slemen	£5.99
LIVERPOOL GHOST WALK	Tom Slemen	£5.99
HAUNTED CHESHIRE	Tom Slemen	£5.99
WICKED LIVERPOOL	Tom Slemen	£5.99
HAUNTED LIVERPOOL ANTHOLOGY	Tom Slemen	£6.99
HAUNTED LIVERPOOL double cassette and audio book read by	Tom Slemen	£8.99

Available from all good bookshops

For a free stocklist contact:

THE BLUECOAT PRESS
329 Mariners House
Queens Dock Commercial Centre
Norfolk Street
Liverpool L1 0BG

Telephone: 0151 707 2390
Website: www.bluecoatpress.co.uk

If you have had a paranormal encounter, or a supernatural experience of any sort, please drop a line to Tom Slemen c/o the above address.